WILD FLOWERS
ON THE EDGE

THE STORY
OF
NORTH YORKSHIRE'S
ROAD VERGES

Margaret Atherden

Nan Sykes

ISBN 978-1-906604-40-0

PLACE Office, York St John University,
Lord Mayor's Walk, York, YO31 7EX.

E-mail: place@yorksj.ac.uk

Website: http:// place.uk.com

Printed by York Publishing Services, 64 Hallfield Road, Layerthorpe, York,
YO31 7ZQ

CONTENTS

INTRODUCTION

What is a road verge?

To many people the road verge is merely a boring strip of grass, seen in a blur when speeding past in a car. Trampled on, strewn with rubbish or mown to within an inch of its life, the typical verge seems to offer little of interest beyond a safe passage for pedestrians beside the busy road. However, for much of our wildlife, the verge forms a natural sanctuary - a green corridor through the countryside, linking up grasslands, woods and wetlands. As this book will show, the road verge network is an important feature in the landscape and has an essential part to play in nature conservation and in the struggle to mitigate the effects of climate change.

The motorist speeding past seldom notices the wild flowers beside the road such as these early purple orchids

The authors have studied road verges in North Yorkshire for over a quarter of a century, recording and photographing their wild flowers and noting their changing fortunes. Our aim in writing this book is to highlight this often overlooked habitat and explain the importance of verges as an essential network for wildlife.

Our focus is on plants, ranging from the common to the very rare, but verges are also valuable habitats for birds, insects, amphibians and small mammals. The book is aimed at anyone with an interest in the natural world on their doorstep and concern for the future of our countryside. The first part of the book looks at the history, uses and characteristics of verges. It considers future management of road verges and shows how they contribute to our natural heritage. The second part describes most of the roadside plants to be found in North Yorkshire and gives hints on identifying them. The final section explains how to get involved in recording verge plants, thereby helping to enhance our roadside flora.

ROADSIDES IN NORTH YORKSHIRE

There are approximately 6000 miles of road in North Yorkshire, most of them fringed by verges varying in width from less than one metre to over ten metres. In towns and villages verges are often intensively managed and lacking in diversity, so it is the rural verges that provide the greatest interest. Each part of the county has its own particular geology and soils, which leads to a great variety of road verge vegetation.

Limestone grassland in the Yorkshire Dales

Heather moorland on the North York Moors

Lime-loving plants, such as mountain pansy, are found on the Carboniferous Limestone of the Yorkshire Dales.

Plants typical of heather moorland grow on the Millstone Grit in Upper Nidderdale and the Jurassic sandstones and shales of the North York Moors.

Most of the low-lying land in the Vales of York, Mowbray and Pickering is covered with glacial drift and intensively farmed, so here plants of neutral soils and escapees from agricultural land are found.

The Chalk of the Yorkshire Wolds has its own characteristic plants, including rarities such as clustered bellflower.

Agricultural land in the Vale of Pickering

Chalk scenery on the Yorkshire Wolds

SEASONAL CHANGES ON VERGES

Seasonal changes are marked on roadsides; woodland verges are at their best in spring while verges adjoining heather moorland burst into bloom in summer. Some flowers, such as moschatel (right) and wood anemone, only show themselves in the early part of the year, dying down after flowering.

A woodland bank of spring flowers

Others, like devil's-bit scabious (left) flower in late summer and are difficult to spot earlier in the year.

The white stars of wood anemones brighten up many road-sides in spring

Verges on opposite sides of the same road may look very different as a result of contrasts in drainage and aspect. For instance, a sunny south-facing verge will have a different flora from a shady north-facing one; a steeply sloping verge that is well-drained will support a different range of plants from a flat, poorly drained one. Road verges and their wild flowers provide a constant source of interest throughout the year and, best of all, they are freely accessible to everyone.

Gorse can bloom at any time of year, hence the old saying, "When gorse is in bloom, kissing is in season". Here it is flowering in spring in a roadside hedge

ANCIENT TRACKS TO MODERN HIGHWAYS

Roadside verges have existed in one form or another as long as roads or tracks have crossed the land but many were not formalised until modern times.

Roman roads

Some of the earliest verges we know about are those on embankments beside Roman roads. The road system was pivotal to the occupation of northern England and some routes still form the lines of major roads today, e.g. Roman Dere Street, which underlies the modern A1. Another major north-south route ran along the eastern side of the Vale of Mowbray. Major east-west routes across the Pennines went up Swaledale and Wharfedale, with a road from Aldborough to near Ilkley crossing Nidderdale. Most of these roads either underlie modern roads or have disappeared from view and can be seen only where archaeologists have excavated them. However, other roads and their verges are still visible in the landscape today as green lanes, such as the one crossing the Pennines from Bainbridge to Oughtershaw, linking Wensleydale to Ribblesdale.

Medieval roads

The Roman road system laid the foundations for much of the later network but medieval roads were maintained to a much lower standard than their Roman predecessors. There are frequent documentary references to muddy surfaces and pot-holes, and many roads were subject to waterlogging, especially in the winter. As the road surfaces tended to be so poor, the routes wandered over a wide area, so the adjacent verges were also changeable and probably lacked much permanent vegetation. Some roads were created in medieval times to connect monastic houses and their granges, such as Mastiles Lane, which linked the Fountains Abbey sheep pastures on Malham Moor to the grange at Kilnsey and survives today as a green lane. There was also a dense network of minor roads, linking towns and villages. Many of these were narrow and winding, skirting the edges of the common fields. Their pattern is preserved in today's sharply bending roads, as seen in parts of the Vale of York. Packhorse tracks crossed many rural areas and some were paved, surviving today as 'trods'; good examples may be seen on the North York Moors.

Drove roads

More substantial were drove roads, like the Hambleton Drove Road, which runs down the western side of the North York Moors. These drove roads were wide and had broad verges, forming a linear grazing strip for cattle as they were driven south from Scotland to markets in York and beyond.

Turnpike roads

Responsibility for road maintenance lay with parishes, often a contentious issue which made it difficult for major improvements to be made. In the eighteenth century, turnpike trusts were established by Acts of Parliament, the earliest ones in North Yorkshire being for sections of the Great North Road from Wetherby to Catterick and beyond (following the line of the Roman Dere Street). Tolls were levied to finance upkeep and improvement of the roads. Most of the major routes were turnpiked between 1740 and 1760, including the major roads across the Pennines, also from York to Northallerton, York to Scarborough and Whitby to Pickering. These roads also gave us a variety of artefacts and buildings, including milestones, signposts and toll houses.

Enclosure roads

During Parliamentary Enclosure in the 18th and 19th centuries, new roads were drawn at specified widths, usually 40 feet along rural roads but up to 100 feet on some major roads. When the central parts of these road surfaces were later converted to tarmac, broad verges were left on either side. Lengthsmen were employed to trim the vegetation and cut drainage channels. Most of the verges thus developed accidentally and were colonised by wild plants as the road network evolved.

The Roman road from Bainbridge to Oughtershaw is still used as a track today and is an impressive feature in the landscape

Top Mere Road, near Kettlewell, is a good example of a green lane on the Pennines, used for moving livestock from winter quarters in the valley to summer pastures on the fells

A typical Enclosure road on the Wolds, following a straight line drawn on a map and occupying a standard width of 40 feet. Wide verges were created when the central part was converted to tarmac

An ancient milestone and waymark

Part of the Hambleton Drove Road on the North York Moors

The A1 trunk road follows the line of the Roman Dere Street

Old Toll House near Whaw, on the road from Arkengarthdale to Tan Hill

A lowland road in the Vale of York curving round the edge of former open fields

Part of the 18th century turnpike road, now the A169 from Whitby to Pickering

Other major routes date from the 19th or 20th centuries, such as the A171 Whitby to Scarborough road

Mauley Cross, one of many old waymarkers which guided travellers across the North York Moors

Today's roads

Many of the modern major routes were established by medieval times, including the roads from Whitby to Guisborough, Whitby to Pickering, York to Scarborough, York to Settle, Skipton to Richmond, and Boroughbridge to Richmond. Only the most recent verges alongside our trunk roads and motorways were deliberately planned and planted. They often include broad, sloping verges seeded with commercial mixtures of grasses and wild flowers. Realignment of some roads has left cut-off stretches which often serve as lay-bys and may have a richer flora than the rest of the roadside.

VERGES HAVE MANY USES

Rural verges formed a minor but important component of the agricultural landscape in the past, many being used for hay cropping or grazing. These traditional uses persist in parts of North Yorkshire, where travellers' horses are tethered beside the road or sheep graze unenclosed land, often seeking out the grassy verge in preference to rougher grass or moorland.

Sheep graze unenclosed moorland verges

Travellers' ponies graze verges

Where wide enough, verges form routeways for pedestrians, horses and other animals, not to mention informal picnic sites and unofficial car parks.

Pony trekking on the North York Moors

Summer picnic on a verge

Cattle use verges between fields and farm

Grit piled on a roadside

Rubbish dumped on a verge

Verges have also been used for storage of a wide range of materials, including logs, hay and straw bales, machinery and piles of grit or salt. They are extensively used as routes for services, such as water or sewage pipelines, cables and telegraph poles.

Bales stored on a verge

There are also some unusual uses of verges, for instance for scarecrow displays or sales of local products.

This 'cash cow' appeared as part of a village scarecrow display

Pipe-laying can destroy verge flora

Hand-carved wooden toadstools for sale

Despite so many human uses, North Yorkshire's verges retain a surprising diversity of wildlife and many provide beautiful displays of wild flowers for passers-by to enjoy. A walk down a country lane can still be an uplifting experience, but sadly many of our floral treasures go unnoticed by the time-hungry motorist hurtling by at ever-increasing speed. One of our great joys in studying road verges over the years has been travelling at a slower speed, allowing us to appreciate this part of our natural heritage.

ZONES AND BOUNDARIES

A road verge may have up to seven different zones parallel to the road. Together they form a suite of distinct habitats.

Close to the road edge is the **splash zone**, where plants need to tolerate being driven over, splashed with mud or sprayed with salt in winter. Only the toughest plants can live in these conditions and typically they grow fast and spread close to the ground. Next is the **short grass zone,** usually mown regularly and dominated by low-growing grasses and flowers like buttercups and daisies.

Behind this, where the verge is wide enough, there is a zone of **longer grassland** cut less frequently. This gives taller grasses and flowers a chance to grow and set seed while providing cover for small mammals. If the back of this zone is not cut for several months, scrub or bracken may encroach on the verge.

These zones form the basic roadside habitats but many verges have other zones behind these, adding to their value for wildlife. Sometimes a **drainage ditch** is found towards the back of the verge, forming a linear aquatic habitat that offers sanctuary to amphibians, dragonflies and wetland plants.

Beyond the ditch there may be a **hedge bank**, which often provides a well-drained slope for other plants such as primrose and wild strawberry. The **hedge** itself forms a linear woodland habitat, especially if it includes mature trees with nesting holes for birds. In other cases, the verge may be backed by a **drystone wall,** which can create a useful habitat for plants such as ferns and a refuge for creatures like lizards.

Of course, not all verges have the full suite of zones. Many are too narrow to support more than a couple of grassy zones and others are too flat to have a drainage ditch or a hedge bank. However, it is the range of different roadside habitats that makes verges so attractive to wildlife and valuable for conservation. In a landscape that has lost so many of its flower-rich meadows, woodlands, ponds and marshes, the roadside zones provide partial substitutes. They also link up surviving grasslands, woods and wetlands, forming a wildlife network across the countryside.

The splash zone is picked out by a pale strip of saltmarsh grass on this verge

A verge with short and long grass zones

The short grass zone forms most of this verge with a few wild flowers surviving at the back

A colourful array of moorland flowers grows on this upland verge

This verge is backed by a drainage ditch and mature trees

Blackthorn scrub overshadows the grass zones of this verge

WILDLFE ON THE VERGE

Plants employ various strategies in order to succeed on a road verge habitat. The dominant plants are usually keen competitors, which can cover large areas and prevent other species from colonising their patch. Examples include butterbur and ground elder.

Common Butterbur

Ground Elder

Many woodland verge plants, on the other hand, grow more slowly and flower before the leaf canopy opens. These plants are able to withstand stresses such as drought, primrose and wood anemone being good examples.

Orange tip on Dog Violet

Primrose

Other species depend on their ability to colonise rapidly, grow fast and spread their seeds efficiently. These are ruderal species such as common poppy and dandelion. Some plants, such as yarrow, white clover and Yorkshire fog, can employ several different strategies and are therefore very common on many road verges.

Dandelion

Yarrow

White Clover

A special group of plants have migrated from coastal habitats to colonise the salt-strewn splash zone. Species such as reflexed saltmarsh grass, Danish scurvy-grass and lesser sea spurrey turn up in increasing numbers along our major roads where salt is spread in winter.

Sea Spurrey

Grassland fungi, too, grow on verges, fulfilling a vital role in breaking down plant litter and recycling dead organic matter, but the above-ground fruiting bodies are not conspicuous in this habitat except at the base of trees.

Fungus

Animals also take various approaches to life on the verge. The high degree of disturbance in many verges means that

Badger killed on the road

Rabbit

the most successful animals are those which are fast movers and can exploit several different sources of food. Many small mammals, such as mice, voles, shrews and rabbits, make their homes in hedge banks and use the grassy zones for feeding, retreating to the back of

Adder

the verge when danger threatens. The corpses of hedgehogs, foxes and badgers attest to the dangers of roadside living, as do the squashed remains of migrating toads. Songbirds, such as robin, blackbird, dunnock and whitethroat, use hedgerows for nesting and feeding. Larger birds usually need mature trees for nesting or roosting but often hunt along the verges; kestrels are a common sight, hovering over trunk road verges, and barn owls may be seen flying low alongside the

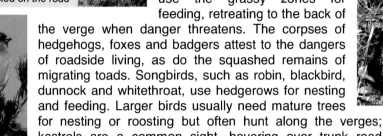
Chaffinch

hedges at dusk. Bats also forage along roadside hedgerows after dark, using verges as corridors through the countryside. A wide range of insects make use of verges, including butterflies, moths, bees, wasps, flies and hoverflies. Nectar-rich wild flowers are the main attraction for feeding, so a good diversity of plants ensures an abundance of insect life. Ants, spiders, woodlice, slugs and snails are amongst the creatures at ground level in the tall grass and hedge bank zones, colonising the litter layer. Common lizards often bask on walls and slow worms may be found in leaf litter below hedge banks. Frogs, toads and dragonflies are attracted to the drainage ditches but need to be mobile, as standing water on verges can evaporate quickly in dry weather.

Red admiral butterfly

Barn owl

Bee on spear thistle

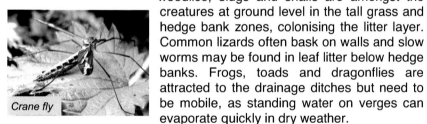
Crane fly

Hedgehog

Dragonfly

Burnet moth

Common blue butterfly

Roadside habitats thus support a large number of wildlife species, especially common and adaptable ones. Most food chains start with plants of the grassy zones or hedge bottoms, so these are vital to the health of the verge ecosystem. However, many species are not confined to the verges but use them as part of wider territories. Perhaps the most important role that verges play is in forming a network of habitats, which enables animals and plants to move around the countryside in response to threats such as climate change. This will be essential for the survival of our wild flowers in the future.

MANAGEMENT

Traditional cutting of road verges was done by hand, using a scythe or sickle. It was a slow, labour-intensive but precise method, allowing each stretch of verge to be managed with care and consideration for wildlife and local needs. However, from the 1960s onwards verge cutting was gradually mechanised, tractors and flail cutters replacing hand tools and enabling verge management to be streamlined. It was faster and more efficient but inevitably verges were managed with less individual care and attention.

Hedges were also cut mechanically rather than by hand with a slasher or

Hand cutting with a scythe in Farndale in the 1980s

Flail cutting has made an unattractive mess of this verge

billhook, often resulting in unsightly broken branches and the loss of many young trees. In the 1950s and 1960s, weedkillers were a popular alternative method of managing verges, with predictably disastrous effects on verge flora and fauna. Mercifully, they are rarely used in rural areas today but are often still applied in towns and villages. Machinery used to manage roadsides has changed over the years and there is now a large range of equipment employed: tractors with side- or rear-mounted cutting bars, huge flail-mowers, small ride-on mowers and mini-balers.

Modern verge cutting by a local farmer

Who looks after roadsides?

Highways Authority verge management

Many different people are involved in managing our verges. Motorways, trunk roads, A roads and B roads are usually managed directly by the relevant Highways Authority, as are junctions and bends on any road where safety is an issue. The cutting of verges along most minor roads is sub-contracted, often to local farmers.

Current management of North Yorkshire's verges is based on a policy agreed between the County Council and the contractor, which sets out the frequency and timing of cutting. However, practice inevitably varies between different sub-contractors and the timing of cutting by local farmers has to fit in with other agricultural work.

Some verges are not cut regularly; others are managed unofficially by local landowners, without reference to the county-wide policy. In a few cases parish caretakers are employed to undertake a range of tasks, which may include verge management. Planting of trees or bulbs is another activity often undertaken by local parishes or individuals. All these different forms of management have implications for the wild flowers and other wildlife on our verges.

Conservation or convenience

Ideally, verges should be managed to enhance biodiversity as well as promote safety and facilitate their many uses. A management system that produces as many different zones as possible will maximise the diversity of both habitats and species. Where verges are wide enough, a tiered system

of mowing is best, with the strip nearest the road cut more frequently than the verge further back. This will produce both short and long grass zones and thus attract a larger number of species than a uniformly mown verge. Frequent mowing in the short grass zone gives a competitive advantage to grasses and other quick-growing plants, whereas occasional mowing in the long grass zone allows taller and slower-growing plants to thrive, thereby enhancing plant diversity, especially on nutrient-poor soils. The best management involves not only tiered cutting of the verges but also removing the cut vegetation.

Wild flowers bloom in profusion on this well-managed, tiered verge

When should verges be cut?

Even where a tiered system of cutting is used, the timing of the cuts is all important for the plants. The best time to cut depends on the species present. Spring flowers will not thrive if the verge is cut early in the year, whereas summer-flowering species will benefit from a spring cut but be prevented from setting seed successfully if cut in June or July. Late-flowering species will not be adversely affected by cutting early in the year but will suffer if cut in July or August. The habitats present and the adjacent land use will usually determine the most

A few common spotted orchids survive at the back of this verge, which was cut in early July when the orchids were in full bloom

appropriate management for biodiversity. For example, verges adjoining deciduous woodland should not be cut before the end of May, whereas verges adjoining moorland are best cut in April or May and again in September. Verges adjoining arable land may be important for the survival of cornfield flowers, which are some of our most threatened plant species. As these plants flourish in the arable cycle, the cutting regime should reflect this, with the verges being cut early in the year and again around harvest time.

Ride-on mowers

An increasing problem on North Yorkshire's rural road verges is the use of ride-on mowers. Country dwellers have traditionally mown the verges immediately outside their gateways to produce a neat and tidy lawn effect, but the advent of the ride-on mower has encouraged some to extend this cutting much further from the gateway and right to the back of the verge. This produces an incongruous strip of closely mown sward with very little in the way of wild flowers.

Tidiness at the expense of wildlife

Obsession with tidiness is leading to deterioration in the flora and knock-on effects on other wildlife, such as small mammals or butterflies. We have seen many once rich verges ruined by over-zealous lawn creation carried out by people who, no doubt, think they are improving the environment.

A verge taken into someone's garden

Occasionally, gardens encroach on to verges, sometimes with stone troughs, rustic bridges and other signs of 'gentrification'. In other areas, farmers seek to increase crop yields by removing hedges, sometimes ploughing almost to the edge of

This verge has been destroyed to increase the size of an arable field

the road and obliterating the verge altogether. Such actions diminish the biodiversity of verges and also deny passers-by the chance to enjoy their wild flowers and other wildlife.

Unnecessarily wide and close mowing has reduced this verge to a boring grass strip of very little interest to wildlife

Here the field extends right up to the road edge, eliminating the verge

An opposite problem occurs on other verges, where cutting has ceased or is so infrequent that coarse grasses, aggressive tall herbs or bracken become dominant and shade out everything else. Scrub development follows eventually and the grassy zones of the verge disappear altogether. There are countless verges in North Yorkshire where this lack of management has resulted in deterioration of formerly flower-rich roadsides. The right cutting regime requires careful planning but is essential for road verges and their wildlife to flourish.

Bracken dominates this uncut verge where once many wild flowers thrived

A formerly flower-rich verge, made coarse and uninteresting through lack of cutting

Yellow-rattle is often used nowadays in conservation management. As a hemi-parasite, it takes some of its nourishment from the grasses amongst which it grows. This restricts the vigour of the stronger grasses, thereby preventing them from dominating the sward and out-competing other plants.

Yellow-rattle

*The presence of **yellow-rattle** on this verge has held back the stronger grasses and produced a diverse flora including the rare **clustered bellflower**.*

By contrast, control by weed-killer has been used on this verge, leaving dying flowers and an unsightly mess of little benefit to wildlife or passers-by.

These two verges show how cutting in tiers encourages a range of wild flowers without traffic hindrance

Imaginative seed mixtures sown on newly established verges can add interest, as in the case of the Harrogate by-pass (above), which was seeded in the early 1990s and retains a varied and attractive flora to this day.

CULTIVATED PLANTS ON THE VERGE

Spanish Bluebell

Cultivated Daffodil

Roadside planting of hyacinths and cultivated daffodils in Nidderdale

A controversial trend in some areas is the planting of cultivated bulbs on rural verges. Whilst splendid shows of golden daffodils in spring look attractive in the vicinity of villages, these cultivated plants are out of place further from habitation and may even out-compete the wild plants. Of particular concern is the danger to our iconic native bluebell by hybridisation from the introduced Spanish bluebell; also threatened by the planting of garden varieties are our native wild daffodils.

Wild Bluebell

Wild Daffodil

A colourful mixture of wild and garden flowers enhances the verge flora on this country lane on the Wolds

Cultivated Gladiolus

*Garden flowers enliven this verge
on the edge of a village*

Other cultivated plants are thrown out with garden rubbish or seed on to verges, where they may be a colourful addition to roadside vegetation but can sometimes dominate native plants if unchecked. Plants to watch out for in this regard include blue-sowthistle, garden goldenrod, honesty and dotted loosestrife. On the other hand, some garden plants have established themselves on verges without spreading unduly and they add to the diversity and interest of the areas where they grow. Examples noted in North Yorkshire include garden campanulas, aquilegias, cyclamen and gladiolus.

Cultivated Campanula

Honesty

Dotted Loosestrife

Blue-sowthistle

CONSERVATION

Road verges form sanctuaries for plants from a range of habitats, including woods, pastures, hay meadows, arable fields, wetlands and moorlands. It is difficult to over-emphasise the importance of verges, both as substitutes for these habitats and as links between their surviving remnants.

Wood Avens

Deciduous woodland was once the dominant vegetation type over most of North Yorkshire but it is now relatively rare in some parts, such as the Yorkshire Dales and the Vales of York and Pickering. Many of our wild flowers started life in the ground flora of deciduous woods and some, such as primrose, wood anemone and bluebell, have successfully adapted to life on the verge. Dog's mercury, and wood avens are common and the woodland buttercup, goldilocks, has also spread on to some sites. Verges, and the hedgerows backing them, form an essential network for these woodland species to spread, as woodland plants are usually poor competitors and spread vegetatively rather than by seed. Ideally, hedges should be cut in an A shape so that plenty of light can reach the ground flora. In some cases, there is no obvious boundary between the verge and the deciduous woodland behind. Some of the most attractive sights on roadsides are seen on wood banks in spring.

Wood Sorrel

Goldilocks

Primrose, Violet, Wood Anemone

Woodruff

Coniferous woodland, often planted by the Forestry Commission, adjoins some verges. Where the verge is narrow and the trees tall and evergreen, deep shade limits the development of the ground flora. Forestry operations also cause considerable disturbance from time to time. However, wide verges can be very rich, especially where limestone chippings have been used for the road material.

A narrow densely shaded forest verge with a poor flora

A wide forest verge with many interesting plants

Some plantations are fringed with deciduous trees, allowing more light to reach the verge vegetation in spring and enabling woodland flowers to thrive. The public forest estate also incorporates many non-woodland habitats within it, including wetlands, old quarries and pockets of farmland. Sympathetic management of verges in these areas makes a valuable contribution to wildlife.

In Dalby Forest on the North York Moors, there are some excellent road verges with rarities such as fly orchid, common wintergreen, viper's bugloss and rock-rose.

Fly Orchid

Viper's Bugloss in an old quarry in Dalby Forest

Domestic cattle grazing a forest verge

Grassland habitats are part of the farmed landscape and some of them are old-established and support a rich flora. Many verges in unenclosed areas of the uplands are grazed by sheep, the verge merging seamlessly into the grassland beyond. Amongst the grassland wild flowers that have colonised grazed verges are commonly bird's-foot trefoil, tormentil and speedwells and occasionally mountain pansy and bird's-eye primrose. However, a well-cut road verge can mimic a grazed pasture, so grazing is not necessary for the survival of these plants. Traditionally-managed hay meadows are rare now, although good examples are protected within the Yorkshire Dales National Park. Road verges are well suited to form substitutes for hay meadows, provided they are managed in an appropriate manner. Plants such as great burnet, meadowsweet, meadow crane's-bill and common spotted orchid all thrive on verges which are left uncut during early summer. In the Dales, melancholy thistle and wood crane's-bill spill on to the verge from hay meadows in Swaledale and Wensleydale.

Common Spotted Orchid

Melancholy Thistle has colonised this verge from the adjacent hay meadow

Bird's-foot Trefoil

Meadow Crane's-bill

In the lowlands, arable weeds that have colonised roadsides include common poppy, field pansy, mayweeds and occasionally corn marigold. These plants need disturbance and lack of competition to survive, so their distribution is erratic. Verges can form links between arable fields and act as reservoirs from which the plants may be able to re-establish by seed in the future.

Corn Marigold

Mayweed

Field Poppy

However, there is another link with arable farming, which is vital for our own survival. The wildflowers of the verges form linear canteens for bees and other insects that perform the vital role of pollination. A wide range of insects is involved,

Foraging bee

Hoverflies

including bumble bees, honey bees, wasps, hoverflies, beetles and flies. They require a supply of flowers rich in both nectar and pollen throughout the spring and summer, so a variety of plants species is needed, blooming at different times of year. Honey bees, for instance, are known to exploit up to 100 different plant species whilst foraging for nectar and pollen. Other bee species specialise, one feeding only on white bryony, others confining their attentions solely to vetches.

Comma butterfly

Small copper butterfly on Scabious

Plants that are particularly good food sources for insects include clovers, daisies, dandelions, knapweeds, campions, bellflowers and heathers. Some species of bees have been lost in this country and several others are now endangered. The abundance of insect life in general has diminished greatly over the past few decades, posing problems for the pollination of some crops. Without the network of roadside verges, pollination in the wider countryside would be less effective, with repercussions for our food supply.

The links between plants and insects are extremely important for the health of whole ecosystems. Even some plants regarded as invasive weeds elsewhere, such as Indian balsam and common ragwort, have their part to play and neither species has become a

Indian Balsam

problem on roadsides we have studied during the past twenty-five years. Ragwort, for instance, is a host plant for the cinnabar moth caterpillar and many other species of butterflies and moths.

Cinnabar moth caterpillars on ragwort

Some roadsides are dominated by large clumps of stinging nettles and these are also useful for conservation, as they are food plants for the caterpillars of several butterflies, including small tortoiseshell and peacock. A well-managed verge with several tiers of vegetation is also important for other insects and spiders.

Drainage ditches backing verges can act as corridors between wetland sites, supporting plants such as pondweeds, milkmaids, marsh marigold and ragged robin. The water supply in the ditches is also essential for many animals, including amphibians and insects. Wetlands are becoming scarce in some areas and maintaining links between isolated sites is increasingly difficult.

Monkeyflower growing in a wetland area alongside a verge

Frog

Roadside drainage ditches are often poorly maintained and easily become overgrown or blocked. Proper management of these features can make a real contribution to the survival of wetland wildlife.

In the uplands, many road verges adjoin **heather moorland.** This is usually managed by grazing and rotational burning, producing a dominance of common heather at the expense

A well managed moorland verge

of most other plants. However, a greater diversity of plants is required for a balanced ecosystem. As the burning does not usually extend right to the roadside, moorland verges can form useful reservoirs of heathland plants, including less common ones like petty whin and cowberry. These in turn support insect life, which provides food for many birds, including red grouse chicks for the first few days of their life. Where moorlands are managed intensively as grouse moors, adjacent road verges can play an important part in supporting wildlife.

THE CHALLENGE OF CLIMATE CHANGE

The importance of road verges for nature conservation is likely to increase greatly in the future, because of continuing human pressure on natural habitats and as a consequence of climate change. Already there are reports of some plants and animals moving in response to the changing environment. Those which grow fast and spread their seeds widely will probably be able to migrate successfully. However, the speed of change gives cause for concern in other cases, especially those species like the woodland flowers that are slow to colonise new sites. Not since the end of the Ice Age have plants had to change their distributions at such a speed …. and then there were no towns, roads or industrial sites in the way.

In Yorkshire, some species are likely to die out, especially those with northerly distributions today, such as cloudberry. This species is very rare on verges in North Yorkshire and is likely to be an early casualty of climate change in our county. Other species with northerly distributions, which may well decline in North Yorkshire as a result of climate change, include globeflower, chickweed wintergreen, marsh hawk's-beard. Another group of plants which may be at risk are species with restricted distributions, such as baneberry, bird's-eye primrose and blue moor grass, all of which occur in a strip from Lancashire to Yorkshire. On the other hand, some southerly species are likely to move north as the

Marsh Hawk's-beard

climate changes, becoming commoner in North Yorkshire, examples being great burnet-saxifrage, white bryony, pepper saxifrage, dropwort, bee orchid and fly orchid. The roadside verge network will play a pivotal role in allowing plants and animals to move freely through the countryside, so it is important that these wildlife corridors are maintained and enhanced by favourable management.

Globeflower

Chickweed Wintergreen

Bird's-eye Primrose

Pepper Saxifrage

Bee Orchid

Road verges form the green threads in a huge network of habitats, linking town and country. Other elements in this network include private gardens, parks, churchyards, brownfield sites, abandoned quarries, riversides, allotments and nature reserves. Together this 'green infrastructure' underpins much of the landscape and provides habitats for wild flowers and animals. The importance of this network for biodiversity has only recently been acknowledged by politicians and the general public but there are encouraging signs that people are at last waking up to the threats to our natural heritage. Many people regret the loss of the flowery meadows and colourful waysides buzzing with insects and ringing with birdsong, which they remember from former years. There is a growing awareness of the damage done to our countryside and wildlife by decades of chemical-based farming and industrial development based on polluting energy sources. The liberal use of insecticides in gardens and an obsession with tidiness have also contributed to the loss of wildlife.

Flower-rich waysides like this were common in the past

Pyramidal Orchid

Whilst it is never possible to turn the clock back, we can move forward in ways that work with nature, not against it, and use modern technology to find alternatives to the excesses of the oil-based economy. At a more local level, we can also ensure that we provide habitats for wildlife in our gardens and along our roadsides. The road verge network could and should be a nationwide nature reserve, to be treasured and enjoyed by both people and wildlife. However, this will only happen if we pass on our appreciation of nature to the next generation. Rachel Carson drew attention in the 1960s to the prospect of a 'silent spring' without birdsong. It is now time to highlight the equally appalling prospect of a countryside devoid of wild flowers, where the children of the future may never be able to marvel at the beauty of a wild orchid or stoop to smell the sweet scent of a violet.

White-flowered Sweet Violet

PLANTS ON NORTH YORKSHIRE'S ROADSIDES

ROADSIDE COMMONERS

Hedge Woundwort Strong-smelling perennial covers long stretches on lightly shaded verges. Erect bristly stalks with coarse pointed leaves have whorls of lipped flowers, beetroot-red splashed white.

Mugwort A tall aromatic perennial common on lowland roadsides with fertile soil. Tall greyish stems with pith inside have long branched spikes of tiny yellowish flowers, almost hidden by woolly bracts. Large leaves white cottony beneath and divided into many narrow segments.

Field Scabious Forms sizeable colonies on well-drained grassy hedgebanks. Hairy waving stems to 1m have large mauve flowerheads edged with spreading petals. Leaves roughly hairy.

Agrimony Tall slender and hairy stems have numerous pairs of alternating large and small leaflets. Long spikes with many 5-petalled yellow flowers June-September. Fruits bell-shaped, circled with small hooked spines. A gregarious plant, plentiful on verges and hedgebanks.

Rosebay Willowherb The most prominent of a large group of plants whose parachute-type seeds ensure widespread dispersal. **Rosebay** produces swathes of tall waving stems with 4 large, widely-spaced, deep pink petals. Very common on roadsides and waste ground. **Broad-leaved Willowherb** is a shorter plant, grows to 60cm singly or in small groups in more shady places. Pink notched petals and round stems. Stigma 4-lobed. Common throughout on hedgebanks and waste ground. **American Willowherb** came to UK in 1891 and has spread rapidly, now often seen on disturbed ground. Pale purple flowers with spaced petals on slightly ridged stems. Stigma club-shaped.

Hedge Mustard Flowers by mid April and through mild winters. Common on waysides. Stiff branched stems up to 1m tall. Leaves with large lobes. Tiny 4-petalled flowers in tight clusters develop into thin narrow pods which are held closely parallel to stalks.

Lady's Mantle takes its name from the leaves - said to resemble a cape. A low-growing spreading and frequent plant with various forms. It has been developed into a showy (but very invasive) garden plant. Bunches of small yellow/green flowers.

Butterbur has rhizomes which enable it to cover long stretches of damp roadside as in Forge Valley near Scarborough. By March, stubby scaly stems emerge topped with small clusters of tubular pinkish florets. Separate female plants very rare. Leaves emerge later and enlarge to 1m across; they were once used as cool wrappers for farm-churned butter.

Crosswort Pointed leaves in whorls of 4 arranged in crosses up unbranched hairy stems. In the leaf axils are densely grouped tiny, yellow fragrant flowers. Frequent on limey grassland.

Hedge Woundwort

Mugwort

Field Scabious

Agrimony

Broad-leaved Willowherb

American Willowherb

Rosebay Willowherb

Hedge Mustard

Butterbur

Lady's Mantle

Crosswort

MORE ROADSIDE REGULARS

Russian Comfrey came to UK in 1870 as a fodder plant. Today this hybrid is our most frequent roadside *Comfrey*. Flowers pink in bud turn bluish as they unfurl on a coiled stem top. Leaves only slightly winged down bristly stems. **Common Comfrey** is a native plant favouring watery places; has crinkly wings all down the stems. Garden escapes seen on roadsides include white-flowered **White Comfrey**, pale yellow-flowered **Tuberous Comfrey** and **Creeping Comfrey** with attractive red-tinted white flowers. Historically *Comfrey* was used as a potage herb and a wound salve, and today's gardeners make a liquid fertiliser from its leaves.

Common Knapweed Also known as *Hardheads.* A frequent perennial on moist grassy verges. Stiff ridged hairy stems have solitary flowers. Short spiky red/purple florets project from a hard, rounded head which is covered with tiny, dark fringed sepals. Simple stem leaves and deeply lobed ground leaves.

Lady's Bedstraw Smells of new-mown hay when dry and was once spread on floors to counteract unpleasant domestic odours. A showy, sprawling plant frequent on dry grassy and rocky ground, especially limestone. Long square stems with whorls of end-pointed leaflets and branched sprays of small golden yellow flowers.

Lesser Burdock A large bushy biennial, often on scrub and waysides. Brush-like heads of purple flowers and large coarse leaves. Hooked bracts on fruit burrs which encourage wide seed dispersal by passers-by also gave inspiration for the invention of modern velcro fasteners.

Yarrow Creates a pale fringe along many roadsides when in flower. Stems up to 40cm have bunches of tiny white or pinkish flowers. Dark green, narrow pointed leaves are divided into numerous thin linear segments.

Winter-cress Grows in colonies on damp grassy verges and ditch sides. Clusters of small, 4-petalled, bright yellow flowers top upright stems. Slender pods held erect. Shiny dark green divided leaves with a large end leaflet. Common.

Hedge Bedstraw clambers across limey hedgebanks and hedgerows, sometimes in large swathes. Groups of small white 4-petalled flowers on branched square stems up to 1.5m. Whorls of 6-8 pointed leaves.

Moschatel Because this carpeting plant has four flowers facing out from a square, plus another on top, it is also known as *Townhall Clock.* From an extensive mat of divided and toothed leaves, erect, short slender stems appear in March, each with a single flowerhead. By May most of the plant has disappeared. Grows in shady woodsides and hedge bottoms.

Ground Ivy Strangely named plant for it resembles ivy only by long creeping and rooting stems. A ground-hugging, hairy perennial with wavy-edged, kidney-shaped leaves on long stalks. Whorls of small, lipped purple flowers open on short upright stems from March onwards. Abundant; sprawling across hedgebanks and bare ground.

Comfrey

Common Knapweed

Lady's Bedstraw

Lesser Burdock

Yarrow

Winter-cress

Hedge Bedstraw

Moschatel or Townhall Clock

Ground Ivy

WOODLAND AND SHADE

Wild Daffodil extends far in some woodland dales and occasionally spreads on to shady verges. Paler and a more elegant plant than most garden cultivars. Grows to about 35cm. Flower trumpets soft yellow with cream outer petals.

Bluebells carpet some old woods often spilling on to an adjacent verge. The native plant has cream anthers and fringed bell flowers hanging on one side of a stem - unlike the introduced Spanish bluebell with purple anthers and flowers arranged spirally around stems.

Lords-and-Ladies or Wild Arum Large glossy leaves in January followed by a thin leaf-like cowl protecting an odorous purple prong (spadix) which attracts insect pollinators. Tiny flowers hidden lower down mature into spikes of scarlet poisonous berries later in the year.

Yellow Pimpernel creeps over damp shady ground. Starry yellow flowers single on short stalks. Pairs of oval pointed leaves.

Dog's Mercury covers dense patches under trees. Tiny, petal-less flowers, male and female on separate plants. No canine connection - just a widespread species.

Wood-sorrel Charming short woodland flower, widespread on shady hedgebanks. Petals white, streaked violet, on slender long stalks. Trefoil leaves pale green.

Bugle Carpets damp shady ground. Short shoots clothed with shiny green/bronze leaves and whorls of blue/purple lipped flowers.

Wood Avens or Herb Bennet On hairy stems, star-shaped flowers with pointed green sepals showing between yellow petals. Burred fruits cling to passers-by ensuring widespread dispersal. Very common on banks and woodsides. Clove-smelling roots when dried said to repel moths.

Water Avens spreads far in damp shady places. Nodding flowers with orange/pink overlapping petals forming a bell surrounded by reddish pointed sepals. Burred fruits.

Woodruff

A faintly aromatic perennial, frequent in lime-rich woodsides. Square stems have whorls of pointed leaves edged with forward-pointing prickles. Small 4-petalled white flowers.

Red Campion

Plentiful in light shade on hedgebanks or woodside. Pink wheel-shaped flowers with darker tubular calyx. Male and female flowers on separate plants.

Yellow Archangel

Yellow flowers, lips streaked orange. Leaves all green in wild plants but silver-splashed in garden escapes.

Enchanter's Nightshade

A spreading perennial plentiful in shade with rich soil. Tiny flowers with two petals on erect stems. Heart-shaped leaves.

Wall → Lettuce

Likes limey soils in woodland shade. Spindly branched stems. Few petals widely spaced.

Wood → Anemone

can cover partly shaded hedge-banks and verges in spring. Solitary white flowers often tinged pink. Hairless leaves deeply divided.

Spurge Laurel

A metre-tall evergreen shrub, rare in lime-rich woods. In early spring, small yellow/green flowers hang in clusters amidst large, leathery dark green leaves. Fruits black and fleshy.

Wood Sage

prefers dry acid soils. Wrinkled pointed leaves. Spikes of pale yellow flowers.

Ramsons or Wild Garlic

Dense, common woodland carpeter, frequent on shady roadsides. White flowers in clusters on leafless stems April-June. Bright green leaves smell strongly of garlic.

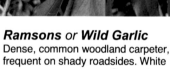

Sanicle

Common on wooded verges with rich soils. Shiny green lobed leaves. Flowers dull white, in tight clusters on long stalks. Fruits covered with hooked spines.

LIME LOVERS

Greater Knapweed grows on lime-rich grassland. Spreading florets fringe large purple flower-heads which grow on metre tall stems, surrounded by deeply segmented leaves.

Common Rock-rose prefers short dry grassy places. Grows a dense mass of tiny oval leaves, white hairy beneath. Yellow 25mm flowers attract many insects. Garden varieties of various colours have been developed from this plant.

Small Scabious Distinguished by black underflower bristles. Slender plant to 70cm. Basal leaves segmented with large end lobe. Narrow upper leaf segments.

Dropwort grows on lime-rich grassland but has become increasingly rare on verges. Delicate pink-tinted flowers held in sprays above finely serrated leaves.

Wild Marjoram forms low, aromatic bushes often seen on lime-rich grassy waysides. It is related to the garden herbs Sweet and Pot Marjorams.

Hoary Plantain grows on chalk and limestone grassland. Waving pink-tinted stamens make a 'fuzzy' flower spike which tops a rosette of hoary or grey felted oval leaves.

Wild Basil is an uncommon plant on dry calcareous verges and quarries. Slightly aromatic mauve flowers, somewhat sparse, in whorls. Sharp green leaves, downy and pointed.

Cowslips spread across many lime-rich lowland verges in early summer. Bunches of flowers hang from each stem - unlike Primrose with its single-flowered stems. Hybrids between these two plants occur.

Dark Mullein has ridged stems to over 1m tall. Dark green hairy leaves. Flower stamens fringed with purple hairs.

Great Mullein has greyish, woolly leaves and stems up to 2m tall. White stamens are orange-tipped. A showy plant welcomed by gardeners.

Modern farm machinery makes light work of the long tough roots of **Common Restharrow,** which, despite its name, is rarely seen on farmland but occurs quite often on sandy or gravely road verges with base-rich soil. Softly hairy leaves. Stems occasionally spiny but not to be confused with *Spiny Restharrow* - a more upright, very spiny southern plant, not known on our verges.

Viper's-bugloss is a bristly erect plant with striking blue/purple flowers. Grows on dry calcareous ground and quarry waste. Its snake-like speckled stalk may have given rise to its strange name. Not a common plant.

Weld is an ancient dye plant, gathered from the wild and grown in cottage gardens by weavers. Tall spikes of 4-petalled flowers on stiff stems with undivided strap-like leaves.

Wild Mignonette Grows in clumps on thin and disturbed limey soils. Lax stems have deeply divided leaves and spikes with small 6-petalled flowers. Slightly fragrant.

Greater Knapweed

Rock-rose

Small Scabious

Dropwort

Cowslip

Wild Marjoram

Hoary Plantain

Wild Basil

Dark Mullein

Great Mullein

Restharrow

Viper's-bugloss

Weld

Mignonette

HERALDS OF SPRING

As soon as winter snows disappear, often in January, pale green shoots, soon followed by **Snowdrop** flowers proclaim the start of a new growing year. A C16th garden introduction, it is a frequent, naturalised roadside plant near villages.

Winter Aconite flowers from February to May. An early garden plant from southern Europe, has a limited lowland distribution in UK. Usually in large swathes under trees on grassy verges.

Although leafy clumps may linger throughout the winter, **Primrose** waits until March to flower. Widespread in light woodland shade on verges.

Lesser Celandine is abundant on grassy verges. Single-stemmed flowers from March until early summer. Up to 12 petals; only 3 sepals.

Barren Strawberry is in flower by February. Sepals show between small white petals. Blunt greyish leaves. Its dry hard fruit is not edible.

Early Dog Violet is usually in flower by late March. Narrow flower with dark spur, not notched at the top. Grows in woodsides and hedgebanks especially on lime.

Sweet Violet has fragrant flowers, sometimes by February. Petals mauve or white. Spreads to cover large patches. Heart-shaped leaves enlarge as flowers fade.

Common Dog Violet flowers about a week later than *Early Dog Violet*. Broad square flower has a pale coloured spur, notched at the top. Our commonest violet, growing in woodland shade and grassland, often on verges.

Hairy Violet has pale mauve flowers, not scented. Hairy stalks and oval pointed leaves. Grows in clumps on limey scrub, occasionally on verges.

HEDGEROW TREES

Many old majestic trees can be seen along our roadsides but younger specimens are harder to find. In the early 21st century, when few hedges are required to provide shade for livestock, most are maintained at around 2m high. Only specifically marked tree saplings are able to mature.

Ash

Oak

Lime

Rowan

Crab Apple

Silver Birch

Sycamore

Scots Pine

Horse-Chestnut

MORE HEDGEROW SHRUBS AND TREES

Hawthorn was extensively planted in new hedges when common land was enclosed from C17 onwards. Still the commonest hedge shrub. Aromatic May blossom grows into round red berries (haws).

Blackthorn Is named after its black bark (unlike pale hawthorn bark) Spiny dark twigs have white flowers in early spring before the leaves. Fruits (sloes) almost black with blue bloom.

Wild Cherry or Gean Attractive tree occasional in hedgerows. White flowers in April produce bunches of small hard dark red cherries. Two tiny reddish glands on stalks near leaf blade.

Field Maple reaches 26m as a tree but more often seen as a hedge shrub. Our only native maple, also planted for its vibrant autumn colours. Straight winged fruits unlike V-shaped wings of sycamore fruits.

Holly was planted both to ward off evil spirits and to provide winter stock feed from its evergreen leaves. Small white 4-petalled flowers precede autumnal red berries. Male and female flowers on separate trees.

Bird Cherry favours damp rich soils in upland valleys. A small bushy tree with white candle-shaped flower sprays. Bitter black berries are enjoyed by birds but not by humans - hence the plant's name.

Snowberry escapes from gardens to from dense suckering hedges. Tiny pink flowers produce white berries which give the plant its name. A North American shrub brought to UK in 1817.

Duke of Argyll's Tea -plant, so called after a mix -up of labels on imported shrubs. A wind-resistant, spiny, spreading bush thrives on coastal hedges. Oval scarlet berries follow pink flowers.

Guelder-Rose A 4m tall shrub frequent on moist ground. Large sterile outer flowers encircle smaller fertile ones on flat sprays. Shiny poisonous red fruits. Leaves turn red/ bronze in the autumn.

Hazel grows 'lamb's-tail' catkins in spring and tasty nuts in late summer. Leaves roundish heart-shaped with hairy stalks. An old coppiced woodland shrub, frequent in hedges.

Wild Privet differs from the widely planted garden hedge privet by its narrower pointed leaves, dark above, light below. Sprigs of white flowers then black berries. Mainly a southern shrub, on calcareous soils, occurs rarely in northern roadside hedges.

Elder Common in hedgerows on nutrient-rich soils. Widely spread by birds which eat the juicy dark purple fruits. These hang in clusters ripened from June sprays of scented creamy-white flowers.

Wych Elm reaches 40m as a tree but is more often a leafy hedge shrub on non-acid soil. Rough pointed leaves have an unequal base partly over-lapping the stalk. Circular winged fruits.

Dogwood A red-stemmed large shrub often in hedge-rows on limey soil. Oval leaves have parallel veins in-curved to the tip. Small 4-petalled white flowers. Black inedible berries.

Mountain Currant Rare native shrub of lime-stone woods; grows in a few hedgerows in North Yorkshire. Flowers small yellowish on erect stalks, male and female on separate plants. Red berries.

Goat Willow A frequent road-side shrub/ tree which produces showy 'pussy willow' catkins in spring. *Bay and Grey Willows* occur in some hedgerows and *Eared* and *Creeping Willows* in the uplands.

MOORLAND PLANTS

Across the hills of North Yorkshire nutrient-poor soils are colonised by a few plants specially adapted to thrive in this harsh landscape. Chief among them is heather or ling which creates a vivid spectacle when flowering at the end of August. Bracken is an on-going threat on well-drained slopes and non-grazed verges. Often on sandy moorland edges gorse takes over. Most of the uplands are grazed by free-ranging sheep which maintain a close-cropped edge along roadsides. Due to constant nibbling, plants here grow in diminutive form but a surprising selection of low-growing tolerant species survive.

Heather *or* **Ling** is the dominant moorland shrublet covering wide expanses of the uplands with a purple haze when in bloom in late August. Home to several specialised birds and

insects and a valuable resource for bee-keepers who move hundreds of hives on to moorland in summer. Controlled burning is practised to maintain young shoots of heather.

Bell Heather favours dry heath, often tumbling down a bank. Bright pink bell-shaped flowers in mid-summer bloom before those of *Heather*.

Tiny dark green leaves with inrolled edges grow up the stem in whorls of three.

Cross-leaved Heath
Indicates wet heathland. Pale pink tubular flowers hang in tight clusters.

Greyish leaves are grouped in whorls of four on downy twigs. Forms patches on damp acid ground.

Bilberry Widespread low shrub of moor and wood with acid soil. Angled green twigs with oval leaves and reddish bell flowers followed by tasty black fruits.

Crowberry Low-growing dense shrublet on upland heath and moor. Red wiry stems with tiny leaves rolled back beneath. Flowers very small. Shiny black fruits.

Cowberry A northern upland shrublet on well-drained acidic soils. Ever-green leaves notched at tip. White open bell flowers. Red berries.

Heath Bedstraw sprawls over acid turf. Tiny white flowers amidst low clumps of pointed leaves, prickle-edged. Common.

Gorse Thickets of prickly, yellow-flowered shrubs line many roadsides on sandy heath and moor. Coconut fragrance when flowering. Pods pop open to fling seeds afar.

Broom Frequent roadside shrub on dry acidic soil. Stiff green angled stems without spines. Bright yellow flowers turn into black hairy pods.

Cottongrasses From April onwards long white cottony hairs of fruiting heads appear on wet peaty verges, replacing earlier unobtrusive brownish flowers. **Common Cottongrass** can spread far. ↓

Tormentil is widespread on upland verges. Low stems have 3 or 5 leaflets. Numerous yellow 4-petalled flowers. The roots give a red dye, formerly used in tanning.

Hare's-tail ↑ **Cottongrass** has an inflated sheath and grows in tussocks.

YELLOW DAISIES
Whichever road you are driving or walking along, you are likely to pass a yellow daisy. At least 25 different species of this varied tribe grow on our verges, ranging from small creepers to showy plants 1.5m tall. A daisy flower is a dense assembly of tiny florets. In some species the small dry fruits are widely dispersed by hairy 'parachutes' blown away from a 'clock'.

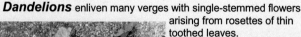

Dandelions enliven many verges with single-stemmed flowers arising from rosettes of thin toothed leaves.

Seeds disperse from dandelion 'clocks'.

Pineappleweed survives trampling in disturbed ground. Yellowish green conical flowerheads on short stalks amidst sprawling leaves. Aromatic when crushed.

Groundsel Common annual weed of waste and bare ground. Yellow disc florets show above tube of long green bracts. May have short ray petals.

Smooth Hawk's-beard
Common wayside plant with clasping leaves on branched, often reddish stems. A fringe of spreading bracts beneath flowers.

Mouse-ear Hawkweed Long runners create extensive mats. Hairy leaves, white felted beneath.

Tansy Flat sprays of small button-like deep yellow flowers; plants to 1m tall and wide. Deeply cut ferny leaves. Strongly aromatic.

Common verge plants with a basal rosette of leaves:

Cat's-ear Single flowers on branched leafless stems which have tiny 'cat's ear' bracts.

Rough Hawkbit Very hairy stems; not branched.

Colt's-foot is in flower by March. Pale, scaly short stems have single flowers. Long-stalked leaves, green but white-felted beneath, appear later. Leaf shape resembles a colt's foot. Widespread on verges.

Autumn Hawkbit Flower stems branched.

Lesser Hawkbit Flower stems not branched.

Prickly Sowthistle has shiny dark green leaves edged with soft spines.

Smooth Sowthistle has light green floppy leaves and pale yellow flowers.

Perennial or Corn Sowthistle grows to 1.5m tall. Large, deep yellow, ragged flowers. Bracts and upper stems covered with sticky yellow hairs. Large green clasping leaves with angular lobes.

Nipplewort Loose sprays of small yellow flowers on tall branched stems.

Corn Marigold Once a common sight on lowland verges. Now very rare - a victim of modern farming.

Common Ragwort is poisonous when cut with hay for stock feeding. In waste ground and on verges it is an important food source for cinnabar moths. Blunt end lobe on toothed leaves. Common on verges.

The less frequent **Oxford Ragwort** has pointed leaf lobes. **Hoary Ragwort** has recurved leaf edges and is mainly coastal.

Rough Hawk's-beard Bright yellow flowers with ruffs of dark-haired bracts.

Goat's-beard flowers are hidden by tall sepals after midday - hence its common name of Jack-go-to-bed-at-noon. Grass-like leaves.

Seed clock

Leopard's-bane ↑
A popular and showy garden plant, occasionally escapes to form large tall clumps near habitation. Bright yellow flowers top waving stems amidst heart-shaped leaves.

Wild Goldenrod Leafy stems with many lax short-stalked flowers. Grows on dry stony or wooded banks.

Hawkweeds show wide variation with more than 260 microspecies. Tall leafy plants often form colonies.

ST JOHN'S-WORTS

ST JOHN'S-WORTS take their name from St John's day on 24th June, their peak flowering time. Historically they were accredited with many mystical powers, good and evil. Today St John's-wort is used in the preparation of anti-depressant drugs.

Perforate St John's-wort
Round stem to 80cm has 2 ridges. Leaves held against the light show mass of pale glands. Dry soils.

Square-stalked St John's-wort
likes damp ground. Reddish square stems to 60cm; large clasping glandular leaves.

Hairy St John's-wort
has a round hairy stem to 1m; black-dotted sepals; hairy leaves. Common on lime-rich hedge-banks.

Slender St John's-wort
Showy small plant with red buds and heart-shaped leaves clasping red stems. Prefers acid soils, often on moorland edges.

Tutsan Native small shrub in damp woods. Large leaves. Flowers to 2cm across; red then shiny black berries.

Trailing St John's-wort Creeping thin stems with pairs of small oval leaves; flowers 8-12mm. Scarce on infertile ground.

BUTTERCUPS   CINQUEFOIL

Meadow Buttercup Smooth branched stems to 1m; indented single leaf lobes. Common on damp soils.

Creeping Buttercup Leaves 3-lobed. Ridged stem to 60cm. Spreads with rooting runners. Very common.

Creeping Cinquefoil grows a mat of 5-lobed leaves beneath its red-stemmed flowers. A frequent prostrate plant in bare or grassy waysides.

Bulbous Buttercup has bent-back sepals and stems swollen at the base. In flower by late March. Prefers lime.

Goldilocks is a distinctive, straggly plant, numerous on moist rich soils Grows 3 types of leaves. Flowers often mis-shapen, petals absent or distorted.

Silverweed is a frequent creeping plant with silvery leaves and single-stemmed flowers from spring until autumn.

CRANE'S-BILLS
Members of the Geranium family, this well-named group of plants have distinctive seed pods shaped like a bird's bill from which 5 segments curl upwards to release ripe seeds.

Meadow Crane's-bill

Widespread on non-acid soils. Large soft blue flowers on hairy stems to 1m tall. Often flowers again after verge cutting. Deeply cut leaves.

Stork's-bill differs from **Crane's-bills** by having pairs of leaflets on a stalk. A low-growing annual, often extensive on dry, sandy ground.

Bloody Crane's-bill Named after its vibrant purple/red flowers. A spectacular but generally coastal plant, also grows on a few North Yorkshire inland limestone verges.

Wood Crane's-bill A northern plant grows in the Yorkshire Dales and Craven. Flowers mauve, usually white-centred on long stalks. Blunt segments on leaves.

Herb Robert
Widespread annual flowers almost through the year. Hairy leaves turn red in autumn.

Shining Crane's-bill
Glossy green leaves, often red tinted. Pointed sepals beneath small unnotched petals. Annual in stony places.

Several attractive introduced crane's-bills grown in gardens become established in the wild. Locally these include:

Dusky Crane's-bill

Hedgerow Crane's-bill

French Crane's-bill

Cut-leaved Crane's-bill Grassland annual. Notched petals shorter sepals. Leaves divided into narrow segments.

Dove's-foot Crane's-bill Low-growing annual common on grassy ground, usually with lime. Soft hairy leaves, roundish with incised edge.

WHITE UMBRELLAS

The opening of white flowers on roadside vegetation is a welcome sight after long winter months. Often known collectively as 'Queen Anne's lace', several species contribute to this display. The order in which they appear helps to identify them. As a family they are commonly known as umbellifers, meaning umbrella-like because their flowers are grouped on stalks which radiate from a single stem like umbrella spokes.

Ground-elder Brought here by the Romans as a culinary and medicinal herb, spreads extensively over many waysides, especially near habitation. Hollow grooved stem; leaves light green and divided into toothed leaflets.

Hemlock A very poisonous biennial of damp places, often in large stands beside ditches. Hairless stems to 2m tall have purple blotches and an unpleasant fusty smell. Irregular, flat umbels of white flowers. Leaves yellowish green, ferny.

Sweet Cicely Aromatic perennial common on Dales verges. Foamy umbels on stems to over 1m. Leaves often white flecked. Pear-shaped blackish fruits.

Wild Angelica Large rounded pink/white umbels on hollow stems to 2m. Lower stems purplish with inflated bracts surrounding leaf stalks. Frequent on damp verges.

Burnet-saxifrage Widespread on well-drained grassland. Tough stems to 70cm with short bracts and narrow divided leaves; root leaves different with oval leaflets.

Cow Parsley Often the first white umbel to flower on roadsides. Downy perennial with hollow stems over 1m. Leaves fresh green, fern-like. Very common from May onwards.

Greater Burnet-saxifrage is ill-named, neither a burnet nor a saxifrage. Ridged hollow stems to 120cm tall. Glossy, dark green leaves coarsely toothed, end leaflet 3-lobed. Umbels wide and flat. Occasional on shady roadsides.

Rough Chervil In flower from June. Ridged solid stems purple-spotted, greyish and hairy, swollen at leaf junctions. White flowers on spaced umbels.

Upright Hedge-parsley A common roadside umbel flowering in July. Solid, rough unspotted stems. Flowers white or pink. Leaves narrowly triangular, deeply segmented, dull green.

Wild Carrot Grows on rough lime-rich grassy areas, especially near the coast. Umbel white or pinkish, often with red centre floret. Flowerhead domed when young, concave in fruit. Prominent bracts beneath. Feathery greyish leaves.

Pignut is named from its edible tuber, formerly relished by scavenging pigs. A plant of old established grassland. Umbels of creamy white flowers in early summer on stems to 40cm. Sprays of finely divided leaves.

Hogweed A large, coarse, hairy biennial named from its pungent smell. Attractive pink-tinted rather flat umbels with spreading forked petals on outer flowers. Leaves with clasping bases, usually broad lobes and toothed edges, but variable.

Ground-elder

Hemlock

Sweet Cicely

Wild Angelica

Burnet-saxifrage

Cow Parsley

Greater Burnet-saxifrage

Rough Chervil

Upright Hedge-parsley

Wild Carrot

Pignut

Hogweed

SMALL WHITE LOOK-ALIKES

Common Chickweed Widespread on waste or grassy ground. Flowers almost throughout the year. Divided petals shorter than pale-edged pointed green sepals.

Thyme-leaved Sandwort Low hairy annual, common on bare ground, walls, waysides. Flowers 3-5mm with petals shorter than sepals. Pairs of tiny, pointed green leaves.

Three-nerved Sandwort Annual sprawler frequent on richer soils. Petals un-notched much shorter than pointed sepals. Oval leaves with 3 conspicuous veins.

Fairy Flax Slender, short annual common on limey turf. Small 5-petalled flowers on waving thin stems. Neat small oval leaves.

Knotted Pearlwort Grows on moor edge and peaty verges. Tight knots of small leaves on thin stems. Flowers 5-10 mm.

Common Mouse-ear Soft hairy leaf pairs resemble ears of a mouse. Widespread, sprawling in drier grassland.

Common Daisy flowers throughout the year in short grassland. Pink-tipped white petals. Basal leaf rosette.

Thale Cress Short, weedy annual often abundant on disturbed ground.

Hairy Bitter-cress Tiny flowers with 4 stamens on straight stems. Common on bare ground and tiresome garden weed. **Wavy Bitter-cress** has 6 stamens, zig-zag stems. Plentiful on streamsides and muddy ground.

Whitlowgrass Under 10cm tall. Tiny flowers have deeply cleft petals. Flat, oval pods. Scattered on bare ground Jan-Apr.

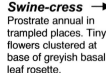

Swine-cress → Prostrate annual in trampled places. Tiny flowers clustered at base of greyish basal leaf rosette.

LARGER WHITE FLOWERS

Greater Stitchwort Frequent on light shady verges from spring onwards. Five deeply-divided petals on 15-30mm flowers. Leaves greyish, narrow; rough, angled stems.

Bladder Campion Clumps occur on grassy or disturbed ground. Tubular flowers have 5 notched petals and inflated papery calyx turning purplish. Leaves greyish, wavy-edged.

White Campion A sticky hairy plant up to 1m tall, occasional on waysides. Five white notched petals and hairy calyx streaked green/purple. Separate male and female plants.

Snow-in-Summer has escaped from gardens to cover wide patches of verge banks and walls. Flowers 10-20mm with 5 shortly-cleft rounded petals. Foliage grey hairy.

Oxeye Daisy or ***Moon Daisy*** has tall waving stems with large flowers and spoon-shaped leaves. Forms colonies on grassy banks.

Lesser Stitchwort has neat flowers 5-12mm. Five split petals appear as 10. Dark green angled stems and narrow leaves. Widespread in acidic grassland.

Field Mouse-ear Rare on dry, calcareous or sandy verges. Erect stems with flowers 6-10mm. Notched, rounded petals much longer than sepals. Narrow, downy leaves.

Wood Stitchwort A northern plant of damp woods or streamside. Flowers 15-20mm have 5 petals deeply divided and widely spaced into 10 blunt segments. Leaves wide oval pointed, pale green.

ORCHIDS

Given a suitable cutting regime, long established grassland, which occurs on many roadside verges but is rare on today's farmland, provides the ideal habitat for orchids. These fascinating plants cannot grow alone - they depend on unseen fungal partners hidden in the soil to thrive - which explains why digging up an orchid to plant in the garden (apart from being illegal) is almost certainly doomed to failure.

Common Spotted Orchid Flowers usually pale pink, etched with darker lines but white forms occur. Frequent on verges.

Common Twayblade Often on grassy verges but not easy to see with an all-green flowering spike and single pair of leaves.

Early Purple Orchid flowers April to June in woodland shade. Its purple (rarely white) flowers have an upward pointing spur.

Broad-leaved Helleborine likes deep shade. Spikes to 80cm tall in late summer.

Northern Marsh Orchid prefers damp ground as its name implies. Its rich purple flowers have up-turned wing petals. Leaves either unmarked or with a few small dark spots near the tip.

Pyramidal Orchid is densely flowered with an earthy scent. It has narrow unspotted leaves and grows on limey soils. Occasionally forms large roadside colonies.

Fragrant Orchid has aromatic flowers with long curved spurs; infrequent on limey grass-land.

Fly Orchid

Both plants occur erratically on verges with short, grassy lime-rich turf.

Bee Orchid

These two orchids have evolved to resemble insects which, when alighting in search of a mate, inadvertently pollinate the flowers.

Bird's-nest Orchid
A parasitic orchid grows in deep shade. Rare on woodland verges. Named from its tangled roots.

Greater Butterfly Orchid A rare aromatic plant of wood and grass-land. Long curved green-tipped spur.

GENTIANS

Autumn Gentian or **Felwort** is scattered in short vegetation on calcareous, often stony soils. Soon disappears with trampling but survives on sheep-grazed turf. Many-flowered stems vary from 2 to 20cm tall. Petals occasionally pink.

Common Centaury An eye-catching biennial in dry grassy ground. Sprays of shell-pink 5-petalled flowers with yellow centres. Erect stems to 50cm. Pointed oval leaves in clasping pairs on stems and in ground rosettes.

Yellow-wort
A yellow-flowered annual rare on short grassy verges with lime-rich soils. Petals close when the sun goes in. Greyish ground leaves, in pairs clasping the stem.

RARITIES

Bird's-eye Primrose*.* Confined in UK to North Yorkshire, Cumbria and Durham where it grows on wet calcareous soil. Named after a yellow 'eye' in bright pink flowers, held erect on mealy stalks. Leaves basal, white mealy beneath.

Baneberry in UK only grows on shady limestone in parts of Yorkshire and Cumbria including a roadside near Helmsley. Fluffy sprays of white flowers. Black shiny berries.

Lily-of-the-Valley Creeping rhizomes make dense spreads in lime-rich dry woodland. Fragrant white bell flowers on one side of short upright stalks followed by red berries.

Saw-wort Scarce at its northern limit in North Yorkshire. Narrow purple flower-heads have tight dark bracts, each pale-edged. Leaves have narrow lobes, edges deeply toothed like a saw.

Herb Paris Occasional on lime-rich wooded verges. Solitary small green flowers then black berries on stems which project above 4 or more prominent leaves.

Musk Mallow Handsome plant with pink or white flowers on tall stems. Long-stalked ground leaves kidney-shaped. Upper leaves deeply divided. Unusual on grassy verges.

Petty Whin Low shrub, scattered on heather moorland, occasional on road-sides. Spiny thin hair-less stems. Pea-type yellow flowers have long lower petal.

Hoary Cress fringes road-sides around Whitby. Masses of tiny white, 4-petalled flowers. Branched stems to c.60cm. Clasping, wavy-edged leaves.

Juniper This evergreen shrub, now increasingly rare, has almost vanished from its Yorkshire sites. A rare stronghold straddles a road-side in Swaledale. Spiny leaves in whorls of 3; tiny cones; blue/black berries.

Ploughman's Spikenard Occasional on calcareous rocky verges. Tall, reddish downy stems have several narrow flower-heads. Deep yellow petals. Large oval, pointed hairy leaves.

Common Wintergreen Forms evergreen patches on woody verges. Short erect stems with small pink/white bells hanging on tiny stalks. Petals hide styles.

Intermediate Wintergreen is similar but styles project beyond petals.

Spindle Small shrub rare in hedge-rows on rich soil. Forked twigs, formerly used by home weavers for winding wool. Pale greenish flowers grow into bright pink and orange fruits.

Common Toadflax but not at all common in N.Yorkshire. Tall stems; greyish leaves. Flowers yellow and orange have long curved spur. Occasional on grassy or disturbed waysides.

Stone Bramble An upland plant near its southern UK limit in North Yorkshire. Creeps on wood-sides with basic soils. Shiny green leaves, few soft spines, upright white petals. Glossy orange fruits have few segments.

Columbine Uncommon tall plant, grows on rocky scrub and wood edge on lime-rich soil. Dark purple flowers have 5 petals with hooked spurs. Garden cultivars have larger flowers with longer spurs and variously coloured petals. Thin greyish lobed leaves.

Pepper–saxifrage A lowland meadow plant found rarely on North Yorkshire waysides. Pale yellow flowers in flat sprays on branched stiff stems to 1m. Large leaves cut into linear segments.

Mountain Pansy An upland plant of lime-rich grazed grassland or lead mining waste. Bright yellow flowers, streaked lower petal, on long slender stalks.

Mountain Everlasting seems to have vanished from some heathy roadsides where it flourished in 1990s. Fluffy pink flowerheads on 20cm stalks; male and female on separate plants. Tiny white-edged leaves.

Bird's-foot Prostrate winter annual on short, acidic sandy turf. Tiny short-stalked flowers. Pods splayed like a bird's foot. Grows on a verge in the Vale of Pickering. (Not to be confused with *Bird's-foot Trefoil*).

DOWN IN THE DITCH

As verge ditches vary from flowing streams of clear water to near stagnant muddy trickles, so their plants range from tiny floaters only 2-3mm wide to tall flamboyant irises. Amongst those recorded are:

Brooklime sprawls far over watery ground and shallow streams. Pairs of oval leaves with sprays of deep blue 4-petalled flowers in their axils. Common throughout the summer.

Water-violet survives in a few roadside drainage ditches cut into wetland in the Vale of Pickering. Its pale mauve flowers arise in early summer from a mesh of narrow submerged leaves.

Several *Water Crowfoot* species grow in roadside ditches. All have 5 white petals, varying in size. The tiny 5mm flowers of *Ivy-leaved Crowfoot* are found in mud; *Common Water Crowfoot* and other larger species grow in wayside streams. Leaf shape helps identification.

Water Forget-me-not is a widespread wetland plant, frequent and extensive along watery banks. The smaller-flowered *Tufted* and *Creeping Forget-me-nots* are less common.

Not to be confused with edible *Water-cress* (see below) is *Fool's Water-cress* which has toothed, bright green leaves and umbrella-type white flowers. But beware of eating it because it closely resembles the highly poisonous *Lesser Water-Parsnip* which has prominent green bracts at stem tops and more deeply toothed, bluish/green leaves.

Monkeyflower fringes many upland streams with its red-blotched yellow trumpet flowers, often creating a colourful roadside ditch.

Yellow Iris Eye-catching on marshy roadsides where it forms large colonies. Stems to 150cm. Large yellow flowers with yellow styles and purple-veined petals. Even taller broad pointed leaves.

Lesser Spearwort takes its name from long lanceolate leaves. Hollow stems sprawl over watery ground, rooting to make large spreads. Yellow buttercup-type flowers on long usually erect stems.

Toad Rush A short, tufted annual, abundant in muddy ground at the water's edge. Greenish/white tiny flowers on much branched thin pale green stems.

Marsh Pennywort Named from its flat coin-like leaf blades held on central stalks. Carpets damp, usually acid ground. Tiny flowers hidden at leaf nodes.

Water-starwort is seen as a mass of small opposite oval green leaves floating in shallow water or mud. Its tiny flowers are rarely seen.

Ragged Robin takes its name from the ragged appearance of its reddish/pink petals which are deeply divided into long, narrow lobes. Upright stems to 75cm with pairs of long, slender, greyish leaves. Can form large eye-catching colonies on damp verges.

Pondweed From a large family of water plants, *Broad-leaved Pondweed* is most frequent as a roadside ditch plant. Recognised by its oval floating leaves and erect flowering stems.

Marsh Marigold Common, often extensive, in ditches and wet grassland. Large yellow flowers on hollow stems grow in extensive clumps with heart-shaped leaves to make colourful displays.

Water-cress Widespread in shallow running water. Sprays of white 4-petalled flowers and leaves divided into roundish lobes with large end lobe. Edible and cultivated as a salad ingredient.

Brooklime

Water-violet

Water Crowfoot

Water Forget-me-not

Fool's Water-cress

Monkeyflower

Yellow Iris

Lesser Spearwort

Ragged Robin

Toad Rush

Marsh Pennywort

Water-starwort

Pondweed

Marsh Marigold

Water-cress

WHERE IT'S WET UNDERFOOT

Verges with marsh, ditch or standing water provide ideal habitats for many specially adapted wetland species. Most are able to withstand temporary flooding or drying out.

Hemp-agrimony Up to 1.5m tall in large stands, usually in damp, lightly shaded places. Leaves divided into 3 or 5 long, pointed lobes, on reddish stems. Clusters of pink, brush-like flowers.

Marsh Valerian Erect stems to 30cm. Lobed stem leaves, ground leaves spoon-shaped on long stalks. Grows in spreading groups on moist soils.

Common Valerian grows to 120cm tall in large groups on wet, often shady, ground. All leaves divided into toothed leaflets.

Water Mint An aromatic, common fresh-water plant. Stems to 60cm have pairs of leaves beneath whorls of mauve flowers with projecting stamens. Clusters of flowers on stem top.

Sneezewort Alleged to cause sneezing by its smell, has also been used to relieve toothache. Flowers with white outer petals and green/grey central disc florets. On wet heath and streamsides with acid soils.

Marsh Hawk's-beard Hairless colonial plant on wet ground in northern hills. Pointed leaves clasp stems to 80cm tall. Deep yellow flowers with black styles.

Cuckooflower or *Lady's-smock* or *Milkmaid* comes into flower in April when cuckoos return here. A frequent perennial on damp grassy ground and ditch-side. Lower leaves with pairs of rounded leaflets, upper stem leaves narrow. Pink or white 4-petalled flowers.

Meadowsweet covers large stretches on moist, non-acid soils. Tall waving stems with sprays of tiny, fragrant, creamy flowers. Long reddish leaf stalks have alternating pairs of large and small toothed leaflets.

Great Willowherb Wetland showy, patch-forming plant. Hairy stems to 150cm have pairs of stalkless pointed leaves. Large deep pink flowers. Similar but smaller, *Hoary Willowherb* has paler flowers and prefers limey damp ground.

Common Fleabane Spreads far in wet grassland and by ditches. Leaves greyish, crinkled. Said to be an antidote to fleas and midges.

Opposite-leaved Golden-saxifrage carpets wide stretches of wetland and stream banks. Tiny 4-petalled yellow flowers appear by April amidst carpets of slightly toothed leaves arising in opposite pairs on creeping stems.
Alternate-leaved Golden-saxifrage has more rounded leaves, crenate-edged, alternately up stems. Less frequent than the above but both species often grow together.

Hemp-agrimony

Common Valerian

Marsh Valerian

Water Mint

Sneezewort

Marsh Hawk's-beard

Cuckooflower

Meadowsweet

Great Willowherb

Common Fleabane

Golden-saxifrage

56

GRASSES form the major part of most roadside verges with over 40 species ranging from tiny prostrate plants to impressive waving stems 3m tall.

False Oat-grass
50-150cm; large roughish leaves; long branched panicles on tall waving stems; awned spikelets.

Cock's-foot
15-140cm; young leaves folded; forms tussocks.

Tufted Hair-grass
20-200cm; forms dense tussocks; coarse leaves sharp-edged; long pointed ligule.

Downy Oat-grass 30-100cm; softly hairy green leaves; bent awns on shiny spikelets. *Meadow Oat-grass* 30-80cm; leaves bluish-green, stiff, hairless. Both on lime-rich soils.

Purple Moor-grass 15-120cm; large tussocks on wet acid soils; narrow purple spikes; ligule of hairs.

Common Bent 10-70cm; widespread perennial; pointed leaves; short ligule; branched delicate open panicle. *Creeping Bent* often sprawls into the splash zone; long ligule; panicle usually contracted.

Smooth Meadow-grass 10-90cm stem smooth; ligule short; leaves blunt or hooded. *Rough Meadow-grass* 20-100cm stem rough; long ligule; leaves glossy below, pointed.

Reflexed Saltmarsh Grass 10-60cm; frequent in splash zone on salt-sprayed roads; lower branches point downwards.

Annual Meadow-grass ⟶
3-30cm; short, pale green, hugs the ground.

Wavy Hair-grass 20-100cm; tightly inrolled leaves; silvery bronze spikelets on open panicles. Abundant on moor and heath.

Couch 30-120cm; spikelets flat against erect stem on alternate sides. **Bearded Couch** has long awns.

Ryegrass 10-90cm; leaves glossy below; oval flat spikelets project sideways on alternate sides of stem.

Meadow Foxtail 30-120cm; spikelets each with one awn; leaf sheath slightly inflated.

Sweet Vernal-grass 10-100cm; hairy auricles; long ligules; aromatic when dry.

Crested Dog's-tail 5-75cm; stiff stem; narrow oblong panicle; spikelets all on one side.

Timothy 40-150cm; spikelets tightly packed, each with 2 awns.

Soft Brome 10-100cm; spikelets softly hairy on short branches.

Wall Barley 6-60cm; flat panicle; bristly awns on spikelets.

Hairy Brome 45-190cm; wide dark green leaves with auricles; lower leaf sheaf has deflexed white hairs; awned florets.

Upright Brome 40-120cm; awned purplish spikelets mostly erect on short branches; upper leaves flat, lower often inrolled; grows in tufts on calcareous soil.

Barren Brome 15-100cm; long nodding branches each with a single long-awned spikelet; soft hairy leaves.

False Brome 30-90cm; leaves yellowish, floppy; stem & leaves hairy.

Yorkshire-fog 20-100cm; soft panicle pinkish buff; grey/green leaves and sheaths softly hairy.

Yellow Oat-grass 20-80cm, shiny yellowish florets; small bent awns.

Mat-grass 10-40cm dark spikelets on one side of stiff stems; wiry leaves; tufts on moorland.

Quaking-grass 15-75cm; flattened oval spikelets on delicate stalks; favours lime-rich ground.

Blue Moor-grass 10-45cm; unusual shiny blue/purple spikes; grows only on Carboniferous Limestone of the Yorkshire Dales.

Red Fescue 30-90cm; leaf sheath downy with reddish base; flowering stem leaves flat. **Sheep's Fescue** 5-60cm; leaf sheath smooth; all leaves thread-like; black roots; on poor soils.

Tall Fescue 45-200cm; wide leaves; hairs on prominent auricles; all branches have several spikelets; forms tussocks, frequent on verges.

Wood Melick 20-60cm waving stems, branched panicles with tiny spikelets; leaf sheath has pointed bristle on opposite side of stem to leaf blade. **Mountain Melick** has spikelets only on one side of stems; rare on verges beside ancient woodland.

Meadow Fescue 30-100cm; branches in pairs, one of each with single spikelet; no awns; hairless auricles. On lowland rich moist soils.

Common Reed Long hairy flowerheads on stems to 3.5m. Leaves 5cm wide, smooth-edged. Often extensive in road-side ditches.

Reed Canary-grass Compact lobed flowerheads on 2m stems. Leaves 2cm wide, rough-edged. Forms large stands.

Wood Small-reed grows in large tussocks. On stems to 2m, oblong flowerheads with tiny one-awned florets. Leaves 1cm wide, rough.

SEDGES are an integral part of roadside vegetation, especially on damp ground. Like grasses they have small rather drab inconspicuous flowers, but differ mainly by their triangular stems. (Grasses have round or oval stems). Of about 70 British species, most frequent on our verges are:

Wood Sedge 15-60cm. Shady woodland, wet soils.

Common Sedge 7-70cm. Damp grassland.

Green-ribbed Sedge to 150cm. Acid grassland.

Bottle Sedge 20-100cm. Water's edge.

Pendulous Sedge 60-180cm. Damp shade.

Glaucous Sedge 10-60cm. Calcareous soils.

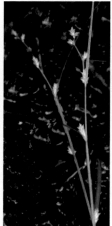

Remote Sedge 30-60cm. Damp woods.

Carnation sedge 10-60cm. Grassland.

Oval Sedge 10-90cm. Acid soils.

Yellow Sedge 20-75cm. Wetland.

Pill Sedge 10-30cm. Dry heath, woodland.

Spring sedge 2-30cm. Dry grass.

Pale Sedge 20-60cm. Clay soils.

Star Sedge 10-40cm. Damp acidic marsh.

Flea Sedge 5-20cm. Calcareous wetland.

RUSHES, HORSETAILS AND WOOD-RUSHES

HORSETAILS have hollow erect stems. Toothed sheaths cover stem joints which may have whorls of side branches. Flowers and leaves absent; cones with spores grow either on green stems or on separate pale stems, usually before the sterile green stems emerge.

Great Horsetail can reach 2m; dull white fertile stems; separate sterile stems emerge later; large spreads on verges with damp, lime-rich soils.

Field Horsetail c.80cm; fertile stems soon die off. Common on wasteland; tiresome weed.

Marsh Horsetail c.50cm; spore-bearing cones on branched green stems. On damp grassy verges.

Wood Horsetail c.50cm; branched drooping stems; separate pale cone-bearing stems. Colonial in woods.

RUSHES Green hairless stems and leaves. Flowers small, brown look-alike petals and sepals (tepals). Wet grassland.

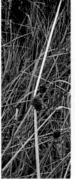

Flowers at stem tops: **Sharp-flowered Rush** Erect stems to 100cm; leaves rounded. **Jointed Rush** To 60cm, half prostrate; leaves flattened.

Heath Rush 50cm stiff matted tufts on moorland. Leaves wiry in ground rosettes.

Soft Rush Smooth stems to 150cm in tufts. Long bracts above flowers. Common on damp grassy verges.

Compact Rush Like *Soft Rush* but ridged stems kinked at flower cluster.

Hard Rush Stems to 120cm. ridged, hard, greyish. Likes lime.

Both wide spread on acidic marshy roadsides.

WOOD-RUSHES have flat, grass-like leaves with conspicuous white hairs and small brown flowers.

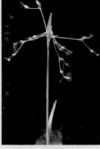

Great Wood-rush grows in large tufts; stems to 80cm, spreads far with runners; wide glossy leaves. Widespread on verges with acid soils beside woods, moorland and streams.

Field Wood-rush (Good Friday-grass) c.30cm; 1 sessile, 3-8 stalked heads; anthers yellow, long. Grassland.

Heath Wood-rush to 40cm; all heads stalked; inconspicuous anthers; follows Field Woodrush. Grassland.

Hairy Wood-rush grows in tufts to 40cm; angular branches have single flowers. Woods, forest and shady verges.

FERNS like partial shade. They are common on roadsides with overhanging woodland. Instead of colourful flowers, they reproduce by tiny wind-dispersed spores on the undersides of fronds. The arrangement of these helps identification.

Male Fern

Lady Fern

Broad Buckler Fern

Lemon-scented Fern

Hard Shield Fern

Bracken

Also on a few of North Yorkshire's upland roadsides are two rare ferns. Both less than 30cm tall with solitary stems. Finding them is a challenge as they are quickly devoured by moor sheep.

Moonwort

Hart's-tongue

Hard Fern

Adder's-tongue

CLOVERS and TREFOILS

Important in any grassland, clovers comprise a large group of plants with an ability to increase nitrogen in the soil. They are important food plants for insects, especially bees.
Flowerheads have a mass of pink, white or yellow tiny flowers.

Red Clover is common on grassy waysides, in flower from May to November. Its white-tinted pink flower-head sits on leaf-like green bracts. Leaves usually have a pale V mark.

Zigzag Clover has pink and white flowers on bare stalks, a zig-zag stem and leaves scarcely or not marked. Favours heavy soils and wood edges.

White Clover produces dull white, maybe pink-tinted, flowers throughout the summer. Leaves usually have a pale V mark. Very frequent on grassy verges.

Alsike has soft pink/white flowers and unmarked leaves. A south European annual used in reseeding mixtures. Occasional on verges.

Hop Trefoil is a scarce annual on lime-rich waysides. Its small pale lemon flowers turn brown and overlap, suggesting a tiny hop cone.

Black Medick is named after its coiled black fruits. Flower-heads bright yellow with downy sepals. Leaflets are downy with tiny end points. Very common on grassy and bare verges.

Bird's-foot Trefoil Common creeping perennial. Red buds open to deep yellow flowers. Seed pods splayed like a bird's foot. Solid, smooth stems to 40cm. ***Greater Bird's-foot Trefoil*** Stems to 1m, hollow, hairy. Grows more upright in damp places.

Lesser Trefoil Widespread on verges. A sprawling low annual with small yellow flowerheads. Distinguished from *Black Medick* by leaflets without end point.

63

VETCHES

Bush Vetch
Common wayside plant, sprawling and climbing with long branched tendrils. Mauve flowers fade with age. Hairless leaflets blunt-ended. Pods black.

Bitter Vetch
Frequent on acidic verges. An erect plant without tendrils, it flowers April-May. Pink petals fade to dull purple. Pairs of narrow leaflets have end points.

Meadow Vetchling
A common scrambler over hedgebanks and verges. Angled stems have long tendrils and pairs of slender pointed leaflets. Yellow flowers develop long black pods.

Wood Vetch Mainly coastal in N. Yorks. Rare on inland hedges. Beautiful pale mauve flowers streaked purple. Stems climb high with tendrils.

Common Vetch Annual on dry waysides. Two-tone pink flowers grow in pairs with black-dotted stipules at base. Up to 8 pairs of pointed leaflets.

Tufted Vetch climbs high and scrambles far with branched tendrils. Up to 40 deep mauve small flowers hang from long stalks June-Aug. Pods brown. Showy and widespread on grassy verges and scrub.

FOXGLOVE

Foxglove brightens many roadsides with acidic soils. This tall attractive biennial is poisonous and should not be handled although it has long been used medicinally to treat heart problems. Various coloured foxgloves are grown in gardens.

CLIMBERS and SCRAMBLERS

Several weak-stemmed plants use hedges as climbing frames to get the light needed to produce flowers and fruits

Dog Rose

Downy Rose

Field Rose

Ivy Evergreen woody climber up trees, bushes, buildings. Greenish flowers in autumn are welcomed by late-flying insects and followed by sooty black fruits.

Wild Roses brighten hedgerows in midsummer; their ripe fruits or hips provide winter bird food.

Black Bryony
At its northern UK limit in North Yorkshire. Shiny heart-shaped leaves almost hide small greenish flowers. Strings of bright red berries - poisonous to humans but eaten and widely spread by birds. Common on hedges with calcareous soils.

White Bryony
A southern climber, rare on northern hedges. Rough square stems with long coiled tendrils. Small 5-petalled greenish flowers, male and female on separate plants, develop sprays of red berries. Large leaves palmately lobed.

Large Bindweed
introduced for gardens in C19th. Now our commonest bindweed, clambering over hedgerows. White trumpets to 9cm across with 2 inflated green bracts.

Hedge Bindweed is a
native lowland species. Trumpets c.3-6cm across. Flat green bracts reveal pale green sepals behind.

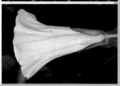

Field Bindweed A native
perennial with underground stems, trails along roadsides and up fences. Scented pink and white striped flowers lie amongst arrow-shaped leaves and tangled stems.

Honeysuckle comes into leaf early in the year and twines up hedge or tree. Sweetly scented flowers from June to Sept. followed by luscious-looking but poisonous red berries.

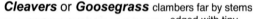

Cleavers or **Goosegrass** clambers far by stems edged with tiny prickles (to the annoyance of gardeners). Tiny white 4-petalled flowers. Whorls of 6-8 pointed leaves. Small round fruits are prickly to enable distribution by passers-by.

ROBBER PLANTS

Most plants use green leaves to convert sunlight and water into essential nutrients but a few have evolved differently. Parasites feed from the roots of other plants while saprophytes rely on decaying vegetation for their food.

Red Bartsia flowers are dusty pink than red despite the name. Frequent grassland semi-parasite.

Eyebright has a long and continuing use as a treatment for eye ailments. Abundant low semi-parasitic annual on short heath.

Common cow-wheat grows on wood banks, scrub and verge. Partly parasitic on nearby plants.

Knapweed Broomrape gets its nutrients from *Greater Knapweed*. Soft yellow spikes appear in midsummer and turn brown before withering. Rare on verges in North Yorkshire.

Toothwort has no green chlorophyll so is totally dependent on other plants for food. Grows at the base of hazel or other shrubs. In flower by April, its flesh-coloured spikes have given rise to the name of 'dead man's fingers'.

Yellow-rattle (or *Hay-rattle* from loose seeds in ripe inflated pods) has green leaves, also takes nutrients from (and stunts growth of) surrounding vegetation. Frequent on verges.

OBSCURE FLOWERS

Spurges are opportunist annuals quick to occupy bare or disturbed ground. Yellow/green bracts replace flower petals. Soft reddish stems contain white juice. Very common.

Petty Spurge Stems have 3 terminal branches. Leaves not toothed.

Sun Spurge Each stem has 5 terminal branches. Leaves toothed.

Procumbent Pearlwort creeps far to form a mossy carpet. Tiny flowers with or without greenish/white petals. Very common on trampled or bare verges.

ROADSIDE THISTLES

Spear Thistle
Common biennial on rough grassy verges. Spiny winged stems to 1.5m tall. Flowerhead bracts and leaves have sharp yellow spines.

Melancholy Thistle
A northern upland plant in old meadows and on a few roadsides in the Yorkshire Dales. Cottony stems to 1.2m have solitary purple flowers. Leaves white cottony below.

Woolly Thistle
A handsome tall biennial of lime-rich grassland at its northern limit in North Yorkshire. The woolly globe covered by spiny bracts has a brush of purple florets. Leaves white woolly beneath.

Creeping Thistle
A persistent perennial on rough grassy roadsides. Spreads by creeping rootstocks and from fragments after verge cutting. Heads pale mauve on bare stems.

Welted Thistle
Tall widely branched perennial occasional on hedge banks. Stems have continuous wavy spine-edged fringe. Spiny leaves cottony beneath. Head bracts spiny.

Marsh Thistle
Very common on dry as well as damp grassland. Groups of small flowerheads on widely branched, often reddish, stems.

Carline Thistle
Prostrate perennial on dry, infertile calcareous soils. Brownish florets ringed by straw-coloured bracts. Dead flower-heads may persist throughout winter.

Musk Thistle
Plentiful on lime enriched soils. Large fragrant and nodding flowerheads are held on tall stems which are bare at the top and have a wavy fringe of spines below.

SALT LOVERS

Throughout the winter when ice or snow threaten to hinder road traffic, tons of salt and sand are spread by mechanical gritters, augmented on hills and minor roads by salt shovelled from roadside bins or salt heaps. From their natural habitats of saltmarsh and sea-sprayed cliffs a few coastal plants flourish in this saline-rich inland habitat where seeds or easily rooted fragments drop from muddy wheels to grow in the splash zones of verges.

Pale mauve flowers of **Danish Scurvygrass** line mile after mile of salted roadsides in some years, although rare on sea cliffs in North Yorkshire. This lowland annual flowers from January.

Reflexed Saltmarshgrass A pale slender grass with down-pointing lower branches. Now very common fringing roads many miles from a saltmarsh.

Common Scurvygrass is abundant on coastal cliffs but rare inland, known only from an upland verge in the Yorkshire Dales. White flowers appear from April.

Not easily seen from a car, nevertheless the tiny flowers of **Lesser Sea-spurrey** abound in the splash zone on many busy roads.

Grass-leaved Orache is steadily moving inland alongside salt-treated roads.

Buck's-horn Plantain occasionally finds a suitable habitat on inland verges far from its natural coastal heath. ←

Saltmarsh Rush (not illustrated) has also been recorded on inland verges in the uplands.

Sea-heath grows on a Ryedale roadside, far from its salt-marsh habitat on southern UK coasts. Not known elsewhere inland.

TRADITIONAL USES OF ROADSIDE HERBS

Selfheal was widely used to staunch bleeding and infused to make a cough cure. Heads of violet flowers on short stalks rise from creeping stems with dull green downy leaves. Very common on grassy and bare ground.

Betony had magical status as a cure for almost any illness - still used occasionally in homeopathic treatments for indigestion and migraine. A frequent grassland plant with an almost rectangular flowerhead and neat bluntly-toothed leaves.

Black Horehound is a strong-smelling perennial reputed to have been used to treat dog bites. Coarse hairy stems up to a metre tall have whorls of dull purple flowers. Occasional on rough ground.

The leaves of *Salad Burnet* have a cucumber taste and continue to be picked for salads. Grows to c.50cm on dry limey grassland in clumps with round red/green flowers. Leaves have up to 12 pairs of small oval toothed leaflets.

Feverfew is an ancient herb, once grown commercially as well as in cottage gardens. Its stringent leaves were used to treat headaches and fevers. Frequent on waysides near dwellings.

Great Burnet grows on heavy clay verges. Up to a metre tall, it has elongated, dark red flower-heads and pairs of red-stalked leaflets. Not known as a salad plant but was a folk remedy to stop bleeding.

Teasel is a striking prickly plant up to 3m tall. Its large conical flower head comprises masses of mauve flowers surrounded by spines. A form with curved spines was grown and used by spinners for carding wool.

Wild Thyme An aromatic low-growing shrublet said to cure plague victims, also used to make a calming tea and as a culinary flavouring. Tiny pink flowers grow amongst dense mats of small oval leaves. Common on rocky heath or short turf.

Common Sorrel A widespread grassland herb away from lime-rich ground. Clusters of small red flowers are held on upright stems with clasping arrow-shaped leaves. These were once used to make a lemony sauce for fish dishes.

Greater Plantain Very common even on trampled waysides. Tiny flowers on a long erect stalk amidst roundish leaves which were chewed or rubbed on a wound to stop bleeding.

Alexanders Restricted to a narrow coastal strip in our region. Plentiful on verges and waste land. Large yellow umbrella-shaped flowers and glossy green leaves on ridged stems to 1.5m. An early pot-herb, also cooked as a vegetable or eaten raw.

Ribwort Plantain is disliked for its irritating pollen causing hay-fever but was valued for leaves used to ease coughs and catarrh. Strongly veined, narrow oblong leaves surround short flower spikes. Abundant on grass and waste land.

69

Selfheal

Betony

Black Horehound

Salad Burnet

Feverfew

Great Burnet

Teasel

Wild Thyme

Common Sorrel

Greater Plantain

Alexanders

Ribwort Plantain

MEDICINAL AND CULINARY HERBS

Fat-hen is frequent on bare verges, especially near salt heaps. Archaeologists have shown that its seeds were eaten by Bronze Age folk and long continued in peasant diets. Annual up to 1.5m has small, mealy flowers and greyish leaves.

Horse-radish was a popular cottage garden plant. Its roots are grated to make a piquant sauce. Although it rarely sets seed, broken fragments easily take root which has enabled horse-radish to spread far on grassy verges.

Usually on more acidic grassland, ***Devil's-bit Scabious*** has pinkish stamens on a rounded mauve flower-head; downy stem and leaves. Flowers June to October. Its short root was thought to have been eaten by the devil to curb the plant's healing powers. The plant was steeped in water to bathe dog bites.

Broad-leaved Dock Widespread tough perennial. Also common is ***Curled Dock*** with its crimped leaves, and in shady ground ***Wood Dock***. Dock leaves are still used to ease nettle stings.

Garlic Mustard (known also as ***Hedge Garlic*** and ***Jack-by-the-Hedge***) is a widespread biennial of woodsides, hedgerows and scrub. Small white flowers April-June on stems to a metre tall. Its garlic-tainted, light green leaves can be used in salads. Formerly used to treat bronchial complaints and worms, also as a poultice for ulcers.

Common Figwort A tall square-stemmed perennial with small brown flowers and large toothed leaves. Common on shady roadsides. Frequent in damp ground is ***Water Figwort*** with a winged square stem, large leaves and 2 small basal leaflets. Because of their pungent smell, they were used to poultice a strong-smelling wound or boiled to make a tonic.

Common Bistort occasionally forms large colonies on damp, grassy roadsides. Its oval, pointed leaves are a main ingredient of a traditional Easter Pudding.

Good King Henry is often found on nutrient-rich soils near old buildings or roadsides. Introduced and grown as a salad plant, it has large triangular leaves and leafless spikes of yellowish flowers.

Soapwort is spread alongside a road in the Vale of Pickering. Once a common cottager's plant used to make a soapy lather, its flowers have also been eaten in salads. Today grown as an attractive pink-flowered border plant in gardens.

Orache is a sprawling plant common on bare and disturbed waysides. Formerly used as a pot-herb.

Shepherd's Purse takes its name from the pouch shape of its seed pods. A variable short, weedy annual, widespread on disturbed ground. Long in use both as salad leaves and to treat kidney problems.

Knotgrass sprawls over bare ground with long wiry stems. Tiny white/green/pink flowers open amidst slender leaves. This plant has an ancient reputation as a cure-all for pig ailments. Very common on waysides and in gateways where it withstands trampling.

Fat-hen

Horse-radish

Devil's-bit Scabious

Broad-leaved Dock

Garlic Mustard

Figwort

Common Bistort

Good King Henry

Soapwort

Orache

Shepherd's Purse

Knotgrass

FOOD FROM THE WILD

Brambles are a favourite hedgerow fruit, gathered in abundance every year to make jam and pies. The plant is notorious for spreading by sending out rooting suckers - a feature that has been used surreptitiously to extend land boundaries. On spiny branches white, or occasionally pink, 5-petalled flowers develop hard red fruits which swell, sweeten and turn black and juicy as they mature.

Dewberry is related to bramble but its fruits, although edible, are tasteless and not worth harvesting. They are smaller and covered with a greyish bloom. Stems are pale green with a few weak prickles. The plant scrambles along hedge bottoms, mainly on basic soils.

Gooseberry is the earliest fruit to be gathered. Spread by birds, its spiny bushes are common in hedgerows and noticeable as one of the first shrubs to show leaves. Tiny flowers are followed by ripe green, later bronze, fruits in May.

Raspberry grows tall untidy clumps, common in hedgerows and scrub, widely dispersed by birds. On prickly stems, white 5-petalled flowers mature into juicy red fruits, easily picked when ripe.

Elder provides two harvests for enthusiasts. Flat sprays of creamy flowers are gathered in late spring to make elder-flower cordial. Later in the year, large bunches of juicy purple/black shiny berries are picked for wine-making. A large shrub or small tree, very common on nutrient-rich waysides and in hedges.

Red Currant is relished by birds which scatter its seeds along hedgerows and on scrub. Small greenish flowers in late spring are followed by bunches of luscious red fruits, valued for home-baking - if they can be harvested before being eaten by birds. Open bushes to 2m tall occur infrequently alongside North Yorkshire's roads.

Wild Strawberry produces small, sweet and tasty fruits, often picked by walkers in late summer. A scrambling plant, common on hedgebanks, with white 5-petalled flowers and tri-lobed shiny green leaves.

Bilberry is an acid-loving plant. extensive on the moors and in upland woods, often bordering a roadside. Forms a low bush with angled green stems, and produces small pink bell flowers followed by dark purple berries. Once sold in local markets, the berries are still picked by home-bakers to make tasty bilberry pies.

Crab Apple is a widespread small tree in hedgerow and copse. Twigs, sometimes spiny, produce beautiful pink and white spring blossom, followed by usually bountiful crops of small, tart apples. These can be gathered to make crab apple jelly.

Blackthorn is well-known for its fruits, long used for making sloe gin. By late March, strongly-spined dark stems produce white flowers before leaves, followed by plum-like fruits covered with a greyish waxy bloom. This large suckering shrub, frequent in hedges, sometimes creates impenetrable thickets.

Hazel is well-known for its dangling yellow catkins in spring. Less obvious are its tiny red flowers which, after pollination, mature into autumn's hazel nuts. A common hedgerow shrub.

NATURALISED FROM GARDENS

Several familiar roadside flowers originated as garden plants, brought in by plant hunters from around the world. Many jumped the garden fence, or were dug up and dumped, to become established wildings on verges and waste ground.

Dame's Violet Named after its origin in Damascus. Leaves spear-shaped. Fruits like a long curved pencil. Flowers white or mauve.

Honesty Grown in gardens for its decorative coin-like silvery fruits. Leaves heart-shaped with toothed edges.

Welsh Poppy Native to Wales and western Europe. Frequent in gardens and naturalised on stony waysides, wood-sides and hedge banks.

Red Valerian Brought from the Mediterranean by Elizabethan plant hunters. Widely naturalised on stony waste and old walls. Flowers pink or white.

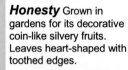

Canadian Goldenrod Stems to 2m. Tiny flowers on one side of curved stalks. Sometimes forms large colonies on verges.

Purple Toadflax From southern Italy this 1m tall plant makes colourful road-side displays. Spurred flowers on waving stems.

Fox-and-Cubs Stems to 40cm covered with black hairs. Clusters of daisy-type orange flowers. Spreads far by runners.

Periwinkles (**Greater** & **Lesser**) From the Caucasus region. Popular in gardens as evergreen ground cover.

Dotted Loosestrife from Eastern Europe soon exceeds allotted garden space - to be dumped on a wayside where it makes large stands. Not to be confused with Yellow Loosestrife, a native riverside plant.

Pink Purslane can carpet a moist open hedge bottom. A short attractive annual from western America. Pink or white flowers in early summer. Spreads far in light shade.

With large, showy flowers, **Blue-sowthistle** is often a gardener's 'must have' - only to be dug up when its rapid spreading habit becomes a menace. Easily roots and spreads on verges.

Indian Balsam Introduced as an ornamental garden plant in 1835, soon escaped to the wild and has become a problem plant on riversides. Occasional on roadsides.

Green Alkanet Thought to be an Elizabethan introduction, now found as a wilding thoughout lowland UK. Spreads to form large stands. Bristly leaves and stems to over 1m.

An attractive rockery plant from the Alps, **Yellow Corydalis** has been grown in our gardens since C17th. Often escapes to walls and rocky roadsides.

Bridewort An ornamental garden shrub from Eastern Europe, sometimes escapes to roadside hedgerows. Waving red stems topped with fluffly bright pink flower spikes. Spreads by suckers.

Because **Greater Celandine** flowers when swallows arrive, it used to be called Swallow-wort. This plant has orange sap and was valued for treating eye-disorders. Occasional, near habitation.

Common Mallow Large mauve flowers made this a good garden plant. Has spread to nutrient-rich roadsides, especially near the sea. Thick circular segmented fruits. A south European plant, now well established in lowland UK.

Winter Heliotrope Fragrant brush-like flowers on short stems appear from Jan on, followed by carpets of cordate leaves. Spreads easily from cut fragments.

Apple Mint A mint hybrid enjoyed by gardeners often escapes to verges near dwellings. Spikes of pale mauve flowers. Crinkly leaves.

NETTLES

White Dead-nettle
Very common in large roadside colonies. Whorls of softly hairy white flowers with black anthers. Leaves have no sting.

Common Hemp-nettle
Roadside annual, small pink or white flowers. Tall square stems swollen where leaf stalks join. Leaves stingless.

Stinging Nettle
Widespread on nitrogen-rich soils where stems to 2m tall can cover larges areas. Leaves have stinging hairs. Tiny male and female flowers hang in catkins on separate plants throughout the summer.
Stinging nettle is a valuable food plant for caterpillars of peacock, red admiral and small tortoiseshell butterflies.

Red Dead-nettle
Low spreading annual common on disturbed ground. Square reddish stems with stalked and stingless leaves. Purple flowers appear all year round.

STRANGE ONIONS
Unusual on our verges are plants of the garlic-smelling onion family. (See also *Ramsons* p31)

Few-flowered Garlic
covers large patches on a few verges. Has several bulbils, few flowers and a single leaf.

Field Garlic
has long thin bracts, green bulbils. Leaves channelled.

Sand Leek
Scattered on a few dry grassy verges. Purple flowers and bulbils. Leaves flat.

Wild Onion or Crow Garlic
usually has a single inflated bract. Narrow V-shaped leaves.

STONE WALLS form boundaries across most of the uplands. Usually dry-stone built without recourse to mortar, they create countless cracks and niches for plants to establish; and make habitats for insects and creatures such as stoats, weasels, adders and lizards.

Ivy-leaved Toadflax

Pellitory-of-the-wall

Rue-leaved Saxifrage

White Stonecrop

Reflexed Stonecrop

Biting Stonecrop

Maidenhair Spleenwort

Wall Rue

Black Spleenwort

SPEEDWELLS have a species to suit almost any habitat so are frequent on various types of verges. They have 4 unequal petals with 2 obvious stamens and leaves in pairs.

Germander Speedwell is very common in grassy places. Reddish stems have 2 lines of hairs. Flowers brilliant blue with white centre.

Heath Speedwell forms dense mats of softly hairy leaves on heath and dry ground. Short upright spikes of lilac flowers.

Wood Speedwell Widespread in light woodland shade. Pale blue/mauve flowers. Neatly toothed bright green leaves.

Wall Speedwell A prostrate, hairy annual on dry soil or wall. Tiny deep blue flowers 2-3mm almost hidden amongst leaf clusters.

Ivy-leaved Speedwell Common, sprawling over disturbed ground. Small lilac flowers appear from March onwards. A form with larger darker flowers occurs.

Slender Speedwell A garden introduction which sometimes spreads to verges. Flowers April - June. Pale roundish leaves.

Thyme-leaved Speedwell forms a mat of shiny, oval leaves. Short erect spikes with small pale blue/mauve flowers.

Common Field Speedwell Low sprawling annual, common on disturbed soils. Lower petal usually white. Light green leaves.

FORGET-ME-NOTS

Wood Forget-me-not is similar to *Field Forget-me-not* but has flatter flowers 6-10cm diam. and petals longer than their tube. Garden escapes with brighter, larger and sometimes pink flowers are quite common.

Field Forget-me-not is one of the commonest wayside plants. Branched stems carry groups of slightly cup-shaped flowers, 2-5mm diam. Sky-blue flowers have 5 petals, shorter than their tube. Downy oval leaves.

Changing Forget-me-not
A short slender annual occasional on dry, often sandy verges. As a coiled flowering stem unfurls, tiny flowers change from yellow to blue.

FLOWER BELLS

Giant Bellflower is a northern plant of fertile hedge-banks and verges, often in light shade. Its metre tall stems carry handsome pale blue flowers from July to September. Bells open to 6cm diameter.

Clustered Bellflower
A plant of southern chalk grassland rare on N. Yorkshire verges. Striking blue/purple flowers in tight clusters. Stems vary from dwarf to 80cm tall.

On dry and heathy grassland, **Harebells** flower from mid-summer until autumn frosts; a delightful plant despite its ancient reputation as the devil's bell or witch's thimble.

FARMLAND FLOWERS

Modern farming methods and herbicides ensure that most of today's arable land is weed-free, but where conservation schemes are undertaken some headlands and field corners enable the survival of a few traditional cornfield flowers. Those with good seed dispersal mechanisms or long seed viability spread to nearby roadsides.

Common Poppy has scarlet petals usually black at the base. Hairy stems.

Poppies have a 'pepperpot' type of capsule which allows seeds to scatter widely. This explains their frequent appearance on verges in arable areas.

Long-headed Poppy & ***Yellow-juiced Poppy*** need more calcareous soils.

← *Redshank*
Reddish stems; small pink/red flowers. Leaves usually with a dark splash.

***Pale Persicaria* →**
Flowers greenish white. Leaves usually without dark marks. Larger than *Redshank*.

Mayweeds Common on bare ground. ***Scentless Mayweed*** has a flat flowerhead. ***Scented Mayweed*** on sandy soils has domed flowerhead, fragrant.

Scarlet Pimpernel
flowers close early and in dull weather. Occasionally creeps along a sandy road edge.

Field Pansy
Small annual often on bare waysides. Sepals show between cream petals. ***Wild Pansy*** Petals purple or yellow conceal sepals. Favours sandy heaths, rare on verges.

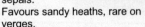

Charlock
Rough-leaved annual very common on dry fields and way-sides.

Oil-seed Rape
Frequent escapee from this widely grown crop. Flowers over-topped by buds.

Wild Radish
Occasional short-lived plant on and near arable land. Flowers with widely-spaced petals may be white, lilac or lemon.

GETTING INVOLVED

During the last few decades, the value of road verges for wild flowers and other wildlife has gradually come to the attention of conservation bodies and local authorities. We began our surveys in the mid 1980s, using a system of colour coding to map the floral diversity of the verges, backed up by detailed studies of the most interesting sites.

Colour-coding scheme for road verges	
Red	Verges of very high plant richness and diversity, including several rare species
Amber	Verges of high plant richness and diversity, including a few rare species
Yellow	Verges with above average richness and diversity but not including any rarities
Green	Average verges, dominated by common species and lacking diversity. This is the commonest type of verge throughout North Yorkshire
Brown	Verges with damaged vegetation, e.g. badly trampled, or intensively managed verges in villages
Mauve	Moorland verges, where heavy grazing pressure prevents plants from reaching their normal potential

We surveyed all the road verges in the **North York Moors National Park** in 1985 and have updated the records since then. Our fieldwork identified more than 170 key verges of particular interest, which are now listed as **'special interest verges'**. Volunteers now monitor these sites regularly, reporting any changes in management or plant diversity to the National Park Authority. The work is co-ordinated by the People, Landscape & Cultural Environment Education and Research Centre (PLACE). On some areas trained Conservation Volunteers carry out practical management work such as scrub clearance, cutting and raking. This means that these special interest verges get management tailored to the particular plant species present, rather than the standard management regime used on most roads. In addition, the National Park Authority has produced a leaflet about the verges and their management, for distribution to farmers, landowners and parish councils.

From 2002 onwards, verges in **Hambleton District** have been surveyed and monitored by volunteers from the C M Rob Natural History Society, and the top thirty-one verges are now managed by staff from North Yorkshire County Council.

Since 2003, the authors have surveyed verges in the **Vale of Pickering,** the **Howardian Hills,** the northern **Wolds** and the **Yorkshire Dales**. These surveys have provided information for several Bio-diversity Action Plans. Our records of plants on special interest verges are also lodged with the North and East Yorkshire Ecological Data Centre, based in York.

In the **Yorkshire Dales**, The Yorkshire Wildlife Trust ran a very successful project in collaboration with the National Park Authority and the Nidderdale Area of Outstanding Natural Beauty. Local communities were approached and several of them got involved in the management of their local verges. A full-time project officer was employed from 2008 to 2011, giving talks, leading walks and producing a newsletter about the road verges project. Since the end of the funded project, some communities have carried on with the management of their local verges and others have joined in.

In the south of the county in **Selby District**, less fieldwork has been done but some local parishes have become involved. For example, North Duffield parish council are now managing their local verges with conservation in mind. Getting local people and groups on board is essential for the future, as it is unlikely that Highways Authorities or other official bodies will have the resources to undertake conservation management of the special interest verges.

© James Ferguson,
Yorkshire Wildlife Trust

If you feel like getting involved, it is advisable to:

> *Be mindful of the traffic hazard and wear high visibility jackets when working on the verge.*
>
> *Equip yourself with identification books and a check list, so that you can make accurate records of all plants present, including grasses. Data collected over several years is particularly useful in assessing the effects of management and climate change.*
>
> *Submit any interesting plant records to the North and East Yorkshire Ecological Data Centre or the Yorkshire Naturalists' Union. Inform the local authority about any problems on the verge.*
>
> *Avoid undertaking any practical conservation work without first contacting the owner of adjacent land and the relevant local authority. If you do get permission to clear scrub or cut a section of verge, when possible cuttings should be heaped towards the back of the verge or taken to a registered tip or green refuse site.*
>
> *Join one or more of the nature conservation organisations that have an interest in road verges, such as The Yorkshire Wildlife Trust, Plantlife or one of the many natural history societies in North Yorkshire.*

Local Involvement

We need to encourage people to take an interest in the wild flowers on their doorstep and adopt their local verges. Keeping records of plants on verges can make a valuable contribution to our knowledge of verge flora and the long-term effects of climate change. Informing local authorities of problems, such as scrub encroachment, dumping of litter or inappropriate mowing of verges, can be useful when decisions are being made about verge management. There is a section on the County Council website where people can report roadside wildlife observations or verges of particular interest. In these ways, everyone can contribute to the conservation of roadside wildlife.

© North York Moors National
Park Authority

Acknowledgements:
Our thanks are due to the many people who have recorded, and continue to record, verge wild flowers across the county and whose records have been made available to us. They are too numerous to name individually but we would like to mention a few persons without whose generous help our task would have been much more difficult. They are: Rona Charles (Senior Ecologist at the North York Moors National Park), Matt Millington (Biodiversity Officer with North Yorkshire County Council), James Ferguson (Yorkshire Wildlife Trust), Brian Walker (Forestry Commission), Phyl Abbott, Deborah Millward, Jill Magee, Jenny Dicker, Polly Millington, Laura Popely, volunteers from the C M Rob Natural History Society and the North York Moors National Park, staff from the North & East Yorkshire Ecological Data Centre, also members of the Yorkshire Wildlife Trust and Yorkshire Naturalists' Union.

Some useful contacts:
Howardian Hills AONB:
   The Mews, Wath Court, Hovingham, YO62 4NN
Nidderdale AONB:
   The Old Workhouse, King Street, Pateley Bridge, HG3 5LE
North and East Yorkshire Ecological Data Centre:
   St William's College, 5 College Street, York, YO1 7JF
North York Moors National Park Authority:
   The Old Vicarage, Bondgate, Helmsley, YO6 5BP
North Yorkshire County Council:
   Biodiversity Officer, County Hall, Northallerton, DL7 9AE
PLACE:
   PLACE Office, York St John University, Lord Mayor's Walk, York, YO31 7EX
Plantlife:
   14 Rollestone Street, Salisbury, SP1 1DX
Yorkshire Dales National Park Authority:
   Yorebridge House, Bainbridge, Leyburn, DL8 3BP
Yorkshire Naturalists' Union:
   c/o NEYEDC, St William's College, York, YO1 7JF
Yorkshire Wildlife Trust:
   1 St George's Place, York, YO24 1GN

Further reading:
Very few books have been published on road verges and their wildlife, although there are many research articles in academic journals on topics such as the effects of salt and the impact of different management techniques. The following books may be useful:

The Roadside Wildlife Book by Richard Mabey (David and Charles, 1974)
Wild Flowers by Sarah Raven (Bloomsbury Press, 2011)
Wild Flowers of Yorkshire by Howard Beck (Crowood Press, 2010)
Picture Guide to the Wild Flowers of North East Yorkshire by Nan Sykes
   (North York Moors National Park Authority, 2008)
New Flora of the British Isles by Clive Stace, 3rd edition (Cambridge University Press, 2010)
A Flora of Wensleydale by Deborah Millward (The Yoredale Natural History Society, 1988)
Historical Atlas of North Yorkshire, edited by Robin Butlin (Smith Settle, 2003)
Plant Atlas of Mid-West Yorkshire by Phyl Abbott (Yorkshire Naturalists' Union 2005)

INDEX

Botanical names follow the *New Flora of the British Isles,* third edition by Clive Stace (Cambridge University Press, 2010). Several have changed since earlier editions.
Many plants have a variety of English names; those most familiar in North Yorkshire are used in this book.